# The Road Rises

## A MEMOIR

### SARAH DUNNE

Published by Mahoe House
Author contact: sarah.dunne.author@gmail.com
www.facebook.com/sarah.dunne.author

DISCLAIMER

The events in this book are true but the names of people, places, and other details have been changed to protect the identities of individuals.

A catalogue record for this book is available from the National Library of New Zealand.

ISBN 978-0-473-69983-3 (Paperback)
ISBN 978-0-473-69984-0 (EPUB)

Cover design: Jeroen ten Berge

# Contents

*For Billy and Ellowyn*

# ONE

# The Woodsman

'THAT'S WHERE I SHOOT WILD SWANS IN THE winter!' Johnny yells, pointing his pole to the headland. 'That's my food all winter. Swan Stew. I soak it in kiwifruit juice to soften the sinews. Then you can eat it, no worries.'

The headland is a dark bump on the lake; the mountains rise black behind it. Johnny splashes his pole back in the water, reaching for the muddy bottom, trying to stop the raft from spinning in the wind. My fingers curl tighter around the boards; water ripples over my wrists.

I call back, 'Do you add anything else to the stew? Or is it just the swan in the pot?'

He half turns and shouts over his shoulder, 'No. I'm looking for a woman who can garden. Can you grow things? My last wife was too lazy. She just lay in the sun reading novels and I had to do all the work.'

I pause, astonished at the notion of a last wife. A wife that would eat wild swans all winter. I shake my head and call back, 'I don't have time. When I come home from work

I'm exhausted, I need to have a rest.' It's all true, the last thing I want to be doing is gardening. Not when I can buy everything cheaper at the supermarket anyway. Not when all I want to do is lie down.

He stops punting. He turns to fully face me, and his eyes gleam. 'Do you have a job? One that earns real money? Steady money?'

I nod. 'Yes, not much money, but it's steady enough and real enough.'

He thrusts his pole in the lake bottom and grins. He stretches one arm high on the pole and puts the other on his hip. 'Looks like I've struck it lucky. I've never had a working wife before. This is going to be great.'

I think I may have just been proposed to. Who knew the only prerequisite for marriage would be a job? It's a little unnerving so I say, 'The wind is blowing us off course. Look, that's where your house is,' I point to a brown speck in the distance, off to the left.

Johnny sets his legs wide and heaves on the pole. He swivels the raft around to set us back on track, but we don't make much headway back down the lake. It's a struggle against the wind, and I realise that all that chunkiness under Johnny's shirt may not be muscle.

After a few punts he turns again, panting, 'I bet you could pick up gardening as well. You look clever enough for that. Together, we could make an excellent stew.'

Out of the corner of my eye I see ducks bobbing in the reeds. I don't point them out to Johnny. Instead, I send them a little prayer. 'Fly away, ducks,' I breathe, 'or you will be cooked up and eaten too.' The wind sloshes waves over the raft. I am wet to my waist and the possibility of sinking is very real. 'Let's stick to the shore; it's safer,' I yell.

He pants back, 'No need, the lake is shallow, 50 centimetres or so. If we sink we can wade out!' He is almost wading as it is, and actually it would be much easier to wade back. I suggest this, but he yells back, 'Yeah, but boating is better. So much fun, eh? Romantic too. I like a bit of romance. That's why I made the lake.'

It takes a while for that to sink in. I look around. This is quite a big lake, quite a thing to have made. The water glints way past the headland, almost to the distant mountain. I say, 'Did you say you made this lake?'

'Yeah,' he yells, 'it was just a swamp so I dammed the river and made it into a lake. Pretty flash, huh? I made the headland too. Just got a digger in for a bit. Swan's head I call it.'

I didn't know you were allowed to do things like this. Dam rivers, turn swamps to lakes, dig headlands. Now I look more closely, the lake is still mostly a swamp. Reeds push up through the water, the wind churns up the muddy bottom and turns the shallows brown. This is definitely still a swamp; it's nowhere near a lake. 'Is this your land, this swamp?' I ask. 'Was it hard to get all the permits to do this?'

'I don't like permits,' he pants. 'I'm my own man, I do what I want, I shoot my own birds, I made my own house, I even made this boat. I'm not one of those soft desk boys.'

Johnny's legs start to shake. I offer to get off to make things easier. For both of us. 'No, no, I can do this. It's easy,' he insists, his face red and mottled. He pushes the pole in hard, bracing himself against it as the raft swings around. We rock, and the waves splash higher.

He turns, 'I make cash too. From the chopping boards. The market where I met you this morning is a gold mine. Today I made enough money to get some petrol for the generator.'

I think of those chopping boards. That's what got me into this date, back at the market in town. Mostly it sold second-hand things, cultural icons from Grandma's house. Except for Johnny's stall. He saw me coming. Saw me licking ice cream with my kids, Billy and Ellowyn, on the park bench long before I had even got into the market. When I wandered past his stall he called to me, he reached his hand out for me to shake. A big thick hand, a well-oiled hand. 'Johnny,' he said.

His chopping boards were dense hardwood, smooth and strong. I picked up a small one. It felt good; it smelt good too. 'Yeah, I knew you would like that,' he said. 'I saw you coming from over there and I said to myself, I bet she likes that board.'

The thing is, we forgot to bring a board on this camping trip. We have been making do with a flat stone back at camp. Billy found it. He likes the stone so much now he has started eating off it too. So a chopping board is exactly what I need.

Johnny showed me his business card. A proper card with a real occupation. 'Woodturner,' it said, and there was a picture of him holding a wooden bowl high and smiling through his dense beard. My imagination took a giant leap. Woodturner could mean he has one of those luxury lodges, full of polished wood and nestled into old trees. It could mean he has hand crafted a wooden yacht for the lake with white calico sails. This chunky, hairy man who sells chopping boards could be my Mr Right.

That's all it took. A well-oiled hand, a business card, the smell of wood. That's what lured me on this wet date.

'Bring your kids too,' he said. 'I like kids. Come for lunch and I will take you all out in my boat.'

Billy refused to come. He wanted darkness after the bright sun in town. He said he couldn't cope with the amount of natural light he was getting. Said his eyes couldn't work in the sun. He went back to bed in his tent, deep in the shade of the trees.

Not Ellowyn though; she loves dates, lunches out, trips in boats. She spent a long time getting ready, putting her hair up, and choosing her outfit. She spent a long time getting me ready too. She piled up my hair, smoothed out one of my crumpled dresses. She had high hopes for this date and buoyed me up too. 'A woodsman, Mum!' she breathed. 'A man of the earth! Just what you should be looking for. He would be great for you!'

But the boat was just a raft and it wasn't sturdy enough for both of us. Johnny wasn't strong enough to punt for both of us. So Ellowyn waited on the shore while Johnny and I went out on the swamp. She lay on her stomach on the bank, keeping a close eye on the raft, waving whenever I turned around.

As we splosh close to land she calls out, 'Is it my turn now? Can I go out in the boat? I want to go to the headland.' Johnny and I clamber off the side and wade in together, pulling the raft behind us. I glance over at him; he looks wrecked. It's clear this punt has stretched him; his whole body is trembling.

'No,' he says, 'I have to show your mum where the vegetable garden can go. Just up here,' he calls over his shoulder. 'This can be your garden,' he lifts his arm and points at a dense stand of flowering gorse. 'You can grow everything here. Good earth under that gorse. You can just clear that out and grow whatever you want.'

The gorse is so thick the earth cannot be seen. What I can see, though, is the steep slope, the blackberry winding through and the thorny trunks of the barberry. It's very clear there are more problems here than just the gorse. That last wife was wise to not even try.

I have been one of those last wives. I have wasted time trying to build good things on steep thorny slopes. I should have just laid in the sun and read novels like this last wife. The result for both of us was obviously the same.

'Best time of year to make a garden. In summertime this town is buzzing, but come winter there's not much money and not much to eat. Got to get the garden ready now. Got to jump on your chances when they come,' Johnny says with a wink to Ellowyn.

I don't think many people have come to Johnny's place. I don't think many even come to his town either. The market this morning was full of stall holders sleeping in the morning sun. I think the summertime buzz could be me. I could be the chance he's jumping on.

Back at his house Johnny drags out two battered chairs for us on the deck, and he perches up on the rail. The deck is rotting through and saplings rise underneath. The forest will overtake this deck very soon. What with all the rain that falls on this coast and the trees pushing through all the cracks.

Johnny goes inside to boil the kettle and put on some music. Enya floats out over the trees, 'Sail away, sail away, sail away,' she sings.

Ellowyn giggles and nudges me, 'Mum,' she whispers, 'is that a sign?'

At the second chorus Enya stops. So does the kettle. There is silence. Johnny comes out and says, 'Right, the water is probably hot enough for tea.'

Johnny has overstretched himself. The generator hasn't pulled through for him, even though he had the petrol money from the chopping board. He rubs his beard and says, 'I thought there would be enough to boil the kettle and listen to the music. But it was only enough for half of that. Should have just done one thing.'

The tea is very cold. If there was ice, it could work as an iced tea thing. But there is no fridge here either. 'In the summer I just stick things I want to keep cold in a bucket in the lake,' Johnny says, 'and in the winter it's cold enough in the house.'

I don't think Johnny is Mr Right. I don't think he is anywhere near Mr Right.

Even though he asked us for lunch, his cupboards are bare, there is nothing to eat. Luckily we brought a big cake. Johnny eats most of it, cutting huge slice after huge slice. 'Hungry work, that market,' he says. 'This is why we need that garden. You can just grow things and make cakes right here. Carrot cake. Zucchini cake. It's all good. I don't mind what you bake.' Ellowyn looks puzzled, 'Gardening? Baking?' She looks over at me, mouths 'What?' and slowly shakes her head.

As we eat, we look across to his swamp, and to his raft tied up to a dead tree. 'I did a good job making that boat,' he says. 'Got those old surfboards from a mate. His kids grew up and didn't want them any more.' The boards do look old.

They have little dents all over them, where bored kids have picked at the polystyrene. 'Found the rope down on the beach, washed off from a fishing boat probably. Good rope though. I just tied the boards together and, yep, there's my boat. Made my house too.'

I turn and look at the house behind me. It is very obvious Johnny made this house all by himself, without any equipment or help. He asks me if I want to look around. I don't. Things look bad. But I go into the kitchen to help return the mugs. Through the slits in the boards I can see sunlight, and even the swamp glinting in the distance. 'Must get cold in the winter, over here, when the wind blows,' I say. It's already cold in the summer; I can feel the wind channelling through these cracks on this fine warm day.

'That's why I keep my long-life milk containers,' he says, holding one up to my face. 'I just rinse them out and then line the house with them. Perfect insulation. By winter this kitchen will be done if I drink milk at the rate I'm going.'

I tell Johnny it's time for us to leave. I've seen all I need to. This is definitely not the luxury lodge of my dreams. Johnny isn't the wild woodsman either.

'But I want to show you my stump!' Johnny says, 'I'm trying to dig it out of the forest. There is good money in that stump if I can get it out.' He takes my hand and pushes in front to lead the way. 'Down here, just squeeze through this gorse.'

But squeezing is impossible. We suck in our stomachs, but still the thorns tear at our clothes. Johnny lets go of my hand and pulls out a knife from his pocket. 'Wait, I will have a go at the path, haven't been out for a while,' he says.

He slashes at the yellow branches stretching high above

us. I don't offer to help, not even to bend them over to make the cutting easier. I've cut enough gorse in my life to cut any more now. I breathe in their coconut smell instead. Johnny's knife isn't the best tool for gorse; it's going to take forever to cut through a tiny branch. A chainsaw is what is really needed here, but I guess we used up all the petrol on Enya.

'Get the keys, fast,' I whisper to Ellowyn. She races back down the path to the deck, then slips the car keys into my hand. 'Johnny, we have to go now, we've got to get back to camp and see if Billy is okay,' I say.

He calls after us, 'But there's the stump! And my workshop! You haven't seen those yet!' And once I get money for the generator, I can make lots more chopping boards.'

We get in the car. I turn the ignition. He leans in the window. 'You will come back, girls. Won't you? Come back and visit me. I will take you out in the boat, Ellowyn, when you come back. We can have cake again. And I will make you stew.'

He waves to us as we leave. 'Great afternoon! See you soon!' he yells.

Ellowyn sticks her arm out the window and waves back as we bump down his rutted drive. My old car seems luxurious after the rotting deck, the freezing house, the swamp. I lean back into the seat and put my foot hard on the accelerator.

'You know, Mum, he could be okay if you dressed him up. Maybe get rid of the beard,' Ellowyn says.

I don't think dressing up would change Johnny one bit, beard or no beard. Besides, there is the house. 'I don't mind the wilderness, but I do mind a freezing house, and I do mind being seen as a pay cheque,' I say.

'Yeah, I don't care about the house, I wouldn't be living there,' she says. 'I'm leaving home soon.' A cold wind blows through me, the one that almost blows me out every time I think of my kids leaving. My girl, leaving home. My youngest. What could possibly fill that space? Certainly not a Johnny.

The roads are gravel and windy on this coast. Even so I drive fast back to our camping spot. The dust clouds up behind us and I feel euphoric. It feels like I've just made a lucky escape. I tell Ellowyn about Swan Stew and Johnny's proposal and we laugh a lot. It feels good to laugh with my girl. I have had so many strange dates now that I'm not too disappointed by this one. In fact, the more strange they are the more I enjoy them in an odd sort of way. It's good to be able to laugh at the end of them.

But, inside, there is a little sigh as well. It would be nice to have my dreams met, just once. 'Anyway,' I say, 'you never know when Mr Right is going to show up. I just have to keep taking my chances.'

Ellowyn turns the music up and we drive through roads with forest on either side. Moss shoulders itself into steep banks, tree ferns umbrella the road, young seedlings push up through the verge. The forest here could reclaim this all in a heartbeat, if it was allowed. I do feel good about that. It's nice to feel that we haven't destroyed everything, and there are still seeds in the ground, strong enough to push through the tarseal. This land does grow strong things.

I hope my kids will be like that too, strong enough to push through their own tarseal. Sometimes I worry that I haven't done enough. And then I worry that I have done too much, that I have fallen into that old trap of living through my kids, and now there is nothing left of me. That cold wind may have more to do with an empty me than an empty nest. Maybe I should be hoping it is me that is strong enough to push through that tarseal.

We drive back to our lake on a road streaming with camper vans. The rainforest, the lakes, the wild beaches pull the tourists in, and it becomes hard to find a secret spot to camp. But even though it's midsummer and more crowded than ever we have a quiet place right on the lake edge. We have to wade knee deep to get to it, but no one minds that. So I park the car and we wade around the corner to Billy and our tents.

I go straight in for a swim. I need to wash off the feelings of Johnny. The sun is low behind me, the water is dark with shadow. It's cold now and the sun has gone, so I swim out a long way to catch its last rays. When I turn and tread water, I see the kids by Ellowyn's tent. They are black shadows in the low light.

The water carries their laughter out to me. I hear bits of sentences, 'Enya, surfboards, cardboard milk containers.' They laugh and laugh. They hold their stomachs, they moan, they roll. Their laughter rings the lake.

I laugh too, way out there. I yell out to them, 'Hey, watch what you say. I might go back for him yet. You know I like a bearded man.' I swim in slowly, quietly, heading for the side bank. The kids have stopped laughing and are now talking, trying to sort me out.

I hear Billy say, 'What is it about Mum? She seems to attract all the weird ones. Who knew there were so many of them? She always has such high hopes, but every date is a disaster. I reckon she should just give up looking and be with Amadou. I like him.'

I sit in the shallows for a bit and think about Amadou. Over the last few years, I have had an on–off relationship with him. There is much to love about him, but he lives in Melbourne and I live in Dunedin. Long-distance things are just too hard, too expensive, too lonely. So at the moment the relationship is off. Mostly it's the logistics. Even though he lives in Australia now, he comes from Guinea, a different culture, a different country. That, and the distance thing is quite hard to navigate. Besides, I have these kids.

'Not for long,' a voice in my head reminds me. And I know this is right. I am on the brink of everything changing.

I make little piles of pebbles in the shallows and think about how it would be to leave my country for a man. It seems an impossible idea, sitting here looking out at this lake. But how would it be to sit in an empty lonely house? How would it be to keep having dates like the one with Johnny? Billy is right, I do seem to attract some strange dates. Maybe New Zealand men just aren't for me.

Billy shouts into the silence, 'Mum, what's for tea? We are starving.'

I realise I am starving too. Ellowyn and I have only had a small slice of cake for lunch, and Billy has had nothing. Ellowyn is ripping through the groceries looking for something instant, but everything needs cooking. It's bad for everyone when she is hungry. I know by the time we get the fire going and cook she will be in a raging fury. Neither Billy nor I could sit that out tonight.

On the drive home I saw a café out on the main road,

'Manu's Pizza, Open Saturday Night', the sign said. Tonight is a Saturday, a great blessing. There is a track through the forest reserve out to the road so we can even walk.

Once the sun goes down it gets cold here. We wrap some blankets around us as scarves and set off. We can smell the wood smoke from the pizza oven through the trees. The café is just a pizza oven that Manu has made in his backyard. It is in the shape of a green dragon whose mouth breathes fire and cooks the pizza. Every Saturday night in the summer he fires up the dragon and whoever wants to join him can come on in.

We sit on old logs in the garden and wrap our blankets around tighter. There is another couple here: American retirees driving around the South Island in a campervan. Manu pokes at the fire, slides pizzas in and out, pours water, enjoys the bustle.

So does Ellowyn. She talks to everyone, she rearranges the stumps so we are all sitting together, she makes jokes, she entertains the Americans. She reads through the menu over and over, even though there are only three options: cheese, pineapple or tomato. She likes all those things, so she chooses them all.

Manu says to Billy, 'Your sister's a real live wire son, she's fun to have around.'

Billy whispers back, 'No, no, it's only because she hates me and Mum. She can't stand us when she's hungry. That's why she's doing this.' He is right. Billy and I have both taken seats as far away from her as we can, and we both have become very quiet.

'Jeeze, you two kids look the same,' the Americans say. I stiffen. This is not a good thing to say. Ellowyn's eyes fill with tears. They don't notice and carry on. They talk about their long straight hair, their big brown eyes, their aquiline noses. They look at them side on and talk of profiles. 'Identical,' they pronounce.

Ellowyn starts to cry. 'That's not true,' she sobs, 'I can't look like Billy. I can't. I can't be that ugly.'

She does look like him. So much so they could be twins.

The Americans look wide eyed, 'We thought it was a compliment,' they say. They give a little laugh, they look around nervously, then at their watches.

Billy meets my eyes over her bent head. He says, 'I'm not that bad, Ell.'

She sobs, 'Yes you are, you are.'

The Americans decide their pizza could be taken away. They have to find a place to stay for the night, before it gets too dark and cold. They squeeze my shoulder, murmur 'Sorry,' then bustle out of the garden carrying their cardboard boxes.

'It's good camping at the lake,' Billy shouts after them.

Manu slides a huge pizza onto a plate in front of Ellowyn. 'Here is your pizza,' he says, 'and you look nothing like your brother.' Ellowyn picks the whole thing up in her hands, she takes big open-mouthed bites, trying to cool it down as she eats. I say nothing. Food is more important than manners at this stage of her rage.

'I don't know why she thinks I look ugly,' Billy says. I shoot him a look, but he won't be stopped. Normally he will let things go, but it seems not tonight. 'Look, Ell, let's measure our noses,' he says. He picks up a long thin leaf and holds it up to his nose. He does have a big nose, even for a boy. He rips it where his nose ends then holds it up to hers.

Hers is bigger. Her nose surpasses the leaf. Billy can't stop laughing. Ellowyn is beside herself. 'It's not true, it wasn't always like this,' she sobs.

Manu suggests another pizza, or maybe dessert? I feel sorry for him, a promising Saturday night has been ruined by a couple of teenagers.

'Stop it son,' I say.

'But Mum,' he says, 'isn't it me who should be upset? I'm the one who's been called ugly. Isn't it me who should be consoled, bought a special dessert?'

Suddenly the notion of the kids leaving home doesn't feel so bad. It would be nice to go out to dinner alone. To eat slowly, to look at the mountains in peace, to be quiet. I think of Johnny eating swan on his rotting deck and at this moment even that would be fine.

We spend the next few days in our own campsite. We lie in the sun reading, being unnoticeable. I don't think other people are good for any of us right now. Ellowyn needs to get over the Americans and her nose. I need to get over another disappointing date. And Billy doesn't like people anyway.

One of the reasons for this camping trip was to get away from people, from phone reception and to force a bit of old-fashioned reading. I'm not sure how much the kids absorb at school; they seem asleep when I drop them off and when I pick them up. So I like to make sure they read some books on holiday.

Billy is delighted with this plan, as long as he can stay in his tent. He powers through books. Ellowyn is harder to persuade. She picks some flowers, does some drawing, lays out all her clothes on the grass and creates outfits. She takes a long time choosing what to wear to paddle around to the jetty.

Our tents all face the water, 'To wake and run into the lake is the best thing to do,' I say, although it's only me that does this. The kids sleep in until lunchtime. So in the morning I have the lake all to myself.

I wake early and watch the trout rise while I drink coffee. Then I pick over the stones and slip into the water to swim properly. I swim out as far as I can while still being able to hear a yell from the tents.

Out here, work fades a little, but I feel the after effects of another hard year. My eye twitches, my heart races. Sometimes it's hard to breathe. I know I have chronic stress; I know I need to change from being a teacher to being something else. But I never seem to have the time to think of what that something else could be. For now, this lake is my recovery centre.

That's what I tell myself every year. Recover first. Then make new plans. Neither of those things seems to happen. My recovery is always partial, my plans nil.

It is a good place to recover though. It's warm here, even when the sun isn't shining. All that heat from Australia gets pushed over on the waves. It makes for a good, cheap holiday, the sort the kids don't mind. Sometimes they complain about the glacial lakes we swim in on the other side of the mountains, closer to home. Over here the weather and the water suits us all.

When the kids wake they hobble barefoot around the stony edge, climb onto the jetty and run and jump into the lake. I sit on the wooden planks, legs dangling into the water, and watch my strong free kids jump high into the late morning sun. They are thin gleaming fish, my Billy and Ellowyn. Cold-water people, born into the icy blue.

'How long do we have left here, Mum?' Billy asks. I am deliberately vague because my real answer is as long as he can stand it. I need them both out of town, all to myself for a while, because I know this is the end. The end of family holidays and kids jumping into the lake. I want to hold on to this as long as I can. For most of their lives it has just been the three of us. But now they are both itching to be proper adults and to go off with their friends. We all know it.

I have been looking around, putting myself out there, seeing if Mr Right is putting himself out there too. But I haven't been looking that hard. I think it could be time to intensify the search. Maybe romance is the thing that could take me in a new direction. I do worry about my heart; I know its palpitations are about entirely the wrong thing. I would like my heart to race in another way, a good way, for my Mr Right.

I eye up the dads hanging around the jetty with their kids. Someone with a boat would be nice. A real boat, not just two surfboards tied together. Mostly, though, the boats around the jetty are kayaks or little blow-up dinghies. I cast my eye out further, looking for something better, looking for a lovely yacht. But the horizon today is empty.

'Watch me, Mum!' Ellowyn calls and I give her scores for height, power, for style. I want to give her a 10 every time, for she has nothing to improve on, this silverfish of a girl. Tall and lythe, she gleams in the sunlight. Sometimes they both run together, they hold hands all the way and fling themselves off as one. And I am extraordinarily happy and sad all at the same time.

Jumping off the jetty and reading become our daily routine. Billy averages one book every two days. Ell struggles through to chapter three of hers. I bargain with her: when she finishes her book I will hire kayaks for us all for the whole day. It will be her chance to get out on the lake after all, and a real lake too, not a swamp.

I do like kayaking; being out on the water is a magical thing. I'm not very good at it though. The kids are fine because of all those Outdoor Adventure classes at school. They get taught kayaking, surfing, rock climbing, snorkelling, all sorts of fun physical things. When I was at school my Outdoor Adventure class was running around the field. Or quietly hiding behind trees.

Still, it's useful having kids that know what they are doing out on a lake so I make the most of it while I can. Billy holds the kayak steady for me, he paddles next to me just in case I fall out and can't get back in. It has happened before. 'Besides,' he whispers, 'I don't want to hang out with Ell. Now her nose is that big.'

Ellowyn paddles ahead of us, blazing the way, trying to see all the things first. She makes a lot of noise with her paddle and points out herons as they rise startled. 'See those birds?' she yells.

Billy isn't interested in seeing anything. He's off in his head making fantasy lands out of the mountains in front of us. His kayak is some sort of mystical craft with billowing sails. In his head on this fine day there are secret paths, men in cloaks, wizards and low-flying dragons. They both seem so young to me still, way too young to be even thinking of leaving. How can you go flatting and still believe in dragons?

That night the kids tell me it's time to go back. They

have reached their limit of being able to stand one another and have already packed their bags. Billy has packed his stone. He recommends leaving the chopping board here. 'We don't need it,' he says, 'not when you have a perfect stone. One stone is all you need for your whole life.'

They miss home, they say. They insist we leave tomorrow. I know it's probably their phones they miss the most, but I also know it's time to go home.

At night the owls start early, hooting from the big totara trees behind us. Billy calls out in a low voice from his tent, 'Mum, can you hear the owls?'

I can. But what I can hear more is my son, who cares enough to notice the owls. And I can also hear in his voice that he's leaving. I can hear him saying, 'Mum, bye, I'm off.' I take some big breaths and hold tight to this moment, all my kids safe in tents at this beautiful place. All of us are here tonight.

It's hard to sleep, and mostly I don't. I think a lot about Johnny, in his windswept house eating wild swans. I can still see the gleam in his eyes when he realised I have a job. I think about that job. I have worked hard at it. I have taken on extra responsibilities, stayed late, networked, and I'm good. I know I'm good. But I have just been passed over for promotion.

'We already have you,' they said.

'We know you won't leave,' they said.

I can still feel the sting of that pass over, the shame, the bitterness. It burns even more in this dark tent far away from it all. And this time, I haven't been able to recover at the lake. Not even a little bit. I feel the same as when I first arrived.

I think I may be in one of those crises, where the stack of

hard things just becomes too much. An empty nest. A dead career. No partner. Failing health.

In the middle of the night, I decided to change everything. I will take back my life. I will leave home when the kids do. I will leave work. I will rent out the house and become one of those backpackers. I will go to all the places I've been dreaming about for years, all those tropical paradises I've seen in brochures. I will swim in the Atlantic, the Mediterranean. I will find my wild roots. I will have adventures, and everything will be different.

I may not have recovered here this time, but I do have a plan. I will escape the shame and the bitterness. I will heal my unease.

I will look for a sweetheart.

I will look for something else, something else.

# TWO

# The Man of God

AUSTRALIA

I FLY INTO THE WALL OF HEAT THAT IS BRISBANE IN December. It's a quick flight, a small step to get my backpacking confidence up. And who knows, maybe Mr Right could be an Aussie. Who knows what my chances are here, what proposals I could get in this lucky country. It has taken me a year to sort out my finances, the house, the kids, work, but here I am. At the beginning of everything new.

But it's hard. Harder than I thought it would be. Brisbane is hot and complicated. It's a struggle to get from the airport into town and to find the place I'm staying. I ease my pack onto my bunk bed. I sit down, put my head in my hands and tell myself I haven't made a mistake. I tell myself the arrival is always the worst thing. Everything will get easier. Fun will happen soon.

Barely able to breathe in the evening heat, and starving, I hunt the streets for food. On a backstreet I come to Govinda's restaurant. Guaranteed good, cheap food. You have to love the Hare Krishnas for their food. With my plate overflowing I hide in a dark corner, at the back, alone.

It's a big night at Govinda's. Soon people are pressing in close around me. Women pull cotton scarves out of their bags and drape them over their heads. Their fingers hover over prayer beads around wrists and necks. The lights are dimmed, there are whispers of gurus. It gets hotter. Layers of thin cotton come off. Jute shoulder bags are piled up around the walls.

I press myself into my dark corner and focus on my food. There is a nice spicy potato dish with black seed things. I look at that, and eat that, and think of how I can slide out of here after I've finished. This food does take a very long time to eat. It's like the magic porridge bowl: the more I eat the more there seems to be. I shovel it in as more people press in.

Musicians shuffle down at the back, next to me, and I realise the room has turned around. The back has become the front, and I am front row. No one else is eating. Someone hisses, 'Wait, you eat at the end, there will be a feast at the end. A Love Feast.'

Tambourines shake, bells and drums jangle and in a cloud of dancing and incense a guru arrives. Orange-robed, head shaved. The Big Deal.

No one else is sitting on a chair. Pressed into the corner, staring at my food, I hadn't noticed the benches being whipped away. Everyone else is cross-legged on the floor, swaying, blissful half smiles on their faces. There is no room to get out. The crowd pushes around me, someone asks to take my chair away.

So I slip off my chair, pull out my scarf, drape it around

my head, and I'm in. It looks like fun could be happening sooner than I thought.

The harmonium breathes out its chords, the guru smiles and breathes into the microphone and we all sway. He calls out the names of God, we call them back; our hand on our hearts, our eyes half closed.

The music fills up the space. The chanting gets faster, the swaying gets wilder, and people have their eyes fully closed. Some clap, and some raise their hands up. And then, suddenly, people are on their feet. They jump up and down, they dance in circles, their hands high in the air, their faces ecstatic.

Then I am up too. I can't be in the front and not dance when all around me everyone else is. For one thing, I'm a bit scared of being trampled. I've read about big concert crowds and death by trampling. These people could squash me and not even know.

So here I am. Dancing and singing in a little hot room in Brisbane, and it's only day one. I dance more and more wildly, for the love of being free and on a crazy adventure. I sing as though my heart is bursting, and it does feel like it is. I fling my arms up for the love of the earth, the love of my children, the love of being free.

Then the music stops. It's over. I have tears running down my face and I'm red and shaking. But everyone around me looks normal and calm. A quiet queue forms at the food counter. As if nothing happened. I join the back of it, needing a drink more than anything. Everyone is polite, self-conscious and reserved. As if we didn't just fling open the universe.

I go back to my corner, with another plate of food.

'Hey,' says a thin bald man wearing robes, 'hey, I really liked your dancing. I'm Satyabhama.' He puts his hands together and gives me a slow bow. 'But you can just call me Shane, that's my real name. I mean, it's my birth name, my Aussie name.'

It seems now I have a friend to sit with for my second dinner. Shane seems very into this whole scene. He has all the gear on for sure. Around his neck are layers of wooden prayer beads. He also has a cross on a chain and a little Buddha charm on a hemp string. It looks like he has all the world's religions happening. I say, 'Tell me Shane, which religion do you follow?'

He goes into a long explanation about Krishna being God and all the other gods are just Krishna by a different name. It seems like having all the cake to me. A big hedging of bets. But I just nod. There is no point getting into any theology, I know those conversations can get tricky fast. So I say, 'Great food. I'm loving this potato thing.'

'Have you read the books?' he asks.

I shake my head. 'No, I don't like religious books. I actually came in for the food.'

He pushes, 'I could give you the books, I have them all at home. You can read mine.'

Needing to get out of this conversation, and seeing the light fading outside, I say, 'I have to go now, I really, really have to go now. I'm new to town, and I need to get home before it's dark.'

His face lights up, 'New to town? Great, I can show you around. Let's have lunch tomorrow, here at 12. Let's have another Love Feast.'

The food is very good here. I have no friends in town

and Shane does seem okay. So I come to Govinda's at 12, and there is Shane. He does look very tired, and very skinny in his normal clothes. It looks as if all his bones are on display in this bright daylight.

I worry about people that look too thin so I say, 'Right, let's have that giant love feast then,' and order big plates of everything. Mostly, everything is pumpkin cooked in different ways, so we have that and take it down the back, to my table from last night.

He pulls hefty books out of his shoulder bag. 'These will save you,' he says, pushing them towards me.

I push them back and say, 'I'm not reading those, Shane, I'm only here for a few days, then I'm meeting my kids in Cairns.' It's a really good excuse, and it's a real excuse. I really am meeting Billy and Ellowyn in just a few days and I can hardly wait. It is my last holiday with them for at least a year, and I want to make it the best I can.

'Hey, me too!' he says. 'My mum lives in Cairns and I'm going up there next week – holidays you know, she gets lonely, you could give me the books back up there.'

I still don't take the books, though I accept his company. We wander round town together. He shows me the art gallery, the river, and the parks. We sit under trees with huge leaves, look at shiny buildings, and Shane talks to me of God.

He says God has punished us by putting us here on earth. The whole planet, not just Australia, was made as a giant prison because we are all sinners.

Inside I'm yawning. Here we go again. Original sin and we are all born bad. I've spent long enough disentangling myself from that one to have any time for it again. Besides, Brisbane doesn't look like a punishment place to me, not any more. It looks like the sort of place everyone wants to live in.

I half close my eyes, lean back and drift off while he tries to convert me. It's fun to watch people hurry through the park, off to work, and to realise that I don't have to do that. I don't have to front up every day and smile and smile. Even just that thought eases my heart a little. I sink into the bench a little more, I slow my breathing and watch life happening around me.

I look at Shane talking on and on. He is passionate about his philosophy, and that is an attractive thing. I wonder how that passion would translate into something else, if it was allowed to.

I see Shane one more time, for coffee. Though he doesn't drink it. He doesn't drink tea either, or alcohol. 'Passion stimulants,' he says, frowning and shaking his head. He doesn't even like sitting in a normal café. He only likes Govinda's: the Hare Krishna café. 'Passion keeps us in this world,' he says. 'I don't do passion.'

I'm so astonished I'm quiet for a bit. Then I say, 'I'm assuming that means no sex as well?'

'No sex,' he says, 'anyway, sex is disgusting. We are disgusting. Our bodies are just disgusting sacks of blood and pus.'

I'm pretty pleased I'm about to leave.

Flying into Cairns in the afternoon is one of the most beautiful things in the world. The plane circles the hills enclosing the town and it looks like the last outpost of the world.

It's January, though, the hot season, and when the doors open on the ground, so do the fires of hell. It feels as if my face could melt off out there. I stand under the fans inside the terminal to wait for Billy and Ellowyn. Worried tourists huddle there with me. I hear them whisper, 'But it looked so great from the air!' and 'Have you tried going outside? Tried breathing out there?'

The shuttle signs say to wait outside at the bus stop, but no one will. The drivers come in and yell, 'Shuttle's going right now. Right Now,' before anyone will leave the fans. I sit on my pack and wait and then suddenly, all in a rush, there they are, my lovely kids. Ellowyn rushes and throws her arms around me. Billy shoves my shoulder with his.

We catch the shuttle into town and drive through empty streets. 'Off season,' the driver grunts, 'too hot out there.' He is right. It seems no one at all is here. No one.

The houses have their windows boarded up. Bristling dogs watch us from behind iron grilles. We are dropped outside our boarded-up apartment. All three of us have to heave on the gate before it clangs open. Inside our room it's dark and cool and no one wants to leave.

'We have to see the place,' I insist.

Billy says, 'This apartment is the place. I will come out only if we look for bookshops.'

Our first stop is the mall. It is air conditioned and everybody is there. The public seats are full of people just sitting and staring, being cool. There are no windows, so no one has to see that the end of the world is just outside the doors. There is a bookshop, but it doesn't sell books, only colouring-in things.

We go out the doors onto the proper streets, where the air has condensed itself into a thick mass and has held everything still for thousands of years. We squint our eyes for protection and walk under verandah overhangs shading the footpath.

Prostitutes lounge against the outside walls. 'Girlfriend, I could get you hot,' one calls out.

Most of the shops are closed for the New Year. We find some second-hand shops and peer through their dusty windows. In the dark, at the back, their bookshelves are crammed full. Billy says he can read their titles. He tells us the best books in the world are in those shops. We read the notices on the glass front door. 'Closed for a month' they say.

Young men lean out of car windows, 'Nnheeer,' they call out to Ellowyn, 'nngheer.' They are deep throated and insistent. Their low-slung car pulses. 'Nnheeer,' they moan.

Ellowyn moves a little closer to me. I say, 'Don't worry, Ell, this is just boys showing off,' but when we get home, she says she's too scared to go out again. She turns the apartment into a cave. She pulls all the curtains and turns the air con on high. Billy says he is too scared to go out too.

So we watch TV in our cave. Australian daytime TV. Bob Saget is our evangelical host. He cries and laughs, he pleads and moans. He raises his hands high in praise of the Lord. Billy loves the theatre of it, he stands up and shouts, 'Hallelujah,' with Bob. He raises his hands high, he yells, 'I'm saved.' Bob walks back and forth across the stage, he hunches over with his head in his hands, sobbing.

Billy and I spend a long time watching Bob Saget and I wonder if Shane watches this too. Now and then Ellowyn yells out, 'Praise the Lord,' from the bedroom where she is talking on her phone.

I do worry about the lack of religious schooling my kids

have had. Will that turn them into a Shane, or a Bob when troubles come? If there is a hole somewhere, it does tend to get filled. Do my kids live in a spiritual hole? And do I?

At the head of the town is the sea. I persuade Ellowyn to take an evening walk with me, to the sea. Billy won't leave Bob Saget. We walk through town in the evening light and the further we get from home the more people there are.

'I think we could be living in the dead end of town, Mum,' Ellowyn whispers.

It is a brown, sludgy sea, a sea guaranteed to have crocodiles. The newspaper says crocodiles have been coming onto tourist beaches lately, but there is no beach here, only a high wall. Even so. We don't sit on the wall.

There is a public swimming pool down here, just in front of the wall. It is magical. There are spreading banyan trees, there is a soft sea breeze and everyone is here.

Even Shane is here. I hear the ting ting ting of the Hare Krishna bells and there he is by the sea wall yelling and jumping up and down. He waves out to me and calls, 'Hey, Sarah, come and join the bliss! come drown in the ocean of transcendental love!'

Ellowyn stops, incredulous. 'Mum,' she hisses, 'you can't, Mum.'

I push some money into her hand for ice cream and say, 'Hey, I have a friend in town, who knew, huh?'

I sit at the edge of the pool, my feet dangling in the water. Shane stops singing, bunches his robes around him and runs over. The jumping has hyped him up. 'I'm in bliss!' he yells to me and the world. 'I'm drowning in ecstasy!'

I see Ellowyn with her ice cream turn around and sit behind a tree on the opposite side. Shane flops down next to me. He pants, 'I have been praying for you, Sarah, praying that you will realise that you are searching for Krishna.'

I smile a little at him and say, 'Shane, I'm not searching for Krishna, I'm searching for Mr Right.'

Shane looks disappointed. He also looks thin, even thinner here than he did in Brisbane. I offer to buy us dinner. 'I can't eat today,' he says. 'Evil has entered all the grain in the world today, and I can't eat evil.'

He slips his feet into the water too, 'Nice feet,' he says about mine. I'm a little startled, but he goes on, 'I really like feet, they are a big thing for us, it's almost like a foot-washing thing, here in this pool,' and he sort of bangs my feet with his.

We talk about his mother for a bit and how hard it is to be old and lonely, and his feet sort of bang into mine a few more times. It could just be the movement of the water, colliding our feet, but I just don't know about that.

The moon rises, full over the water. Shane points to it and says, 'Can you believe people actually believe in moon landings? And there are people that actually think the earth is round!' He gives a little laugh, 'People are so deluded.'

I look at him, astonished, and say, 'Didn't you go to school, Shane? Didn't you do science class?'

He says, 'All science is a fabrication, a giant hoax.' But he goes red. Bright red.

When we get home, Billy has found *Australian Truckers* on TV. This seems to be an adult version of Thomas the Tank Engine. It has real trucks and real men, not cartoons, but otherwise the script is the same. Will the bridge hold out? Will they make it through the traffic lights? Will the boat fall off the trailer? 'Australian TV is the best,' Billy says.

I coax the kids out of the cave with a trip to the Great Barrier Reef. I want them to see the whole glory of the reef, while they still can. I want to give them something to remember. It's a long boat trip out to sea to find the glory though. After half an hour we lose sight of land. Australia seems way too big to lose sight of that quickly, and it unnerves me. We rock up and down on the swell. Alone.

Billy mutters about krakens; he leans over the side checking for tentacles. He murmurs to Ellowyn of shipwrecks, drownings, mutinies. The horizon line looks very close suddenly. We are in a small world where hot troubles could close in.

Nervously we zip ourselves into anti-sting suits. We pull hoods down low over our foreheads, we cover up our chins. Someone whispers they think they just saw a shark. I think of those Australian sea stories, of tourists disappearing on trips just like this, of boats leaving without proper head counts. Of terrible things.

It's an act of courage getting into the water. I hang on to the side of the boat, looking out for black fins cutting quickly through the waves. I call out to the kids, 'Be careful, stay close to the boat, hang on to the boat, like me.'

It's not until I put my head under that all my fears wash away. Deep below tiny fish flicker among the coral. A sea turtle swims in shafts of sun. I let go of the boat and hover above it. Time becomes ancient and slow.

I find Ellowyn and we snorkel along together, pointing things out to each other: long swordfish, starfish, thin colourful pipers. I grab her hand, overwhelmed with love. This is the last time I will see her for a long time, and here we are gasping at one of the great wonders of the world together.

We snorkel for a long time, hand in hand. Then we come up for a rest, laughing, spitting the snorkel out and clearing our masks. And it's not Ellowyn at all. It's an old lady from Germany. Still, I love her anyway, it's that sort of day.

Lunch is included. Shockingly, it's a seafood buffet. We are eating what we have just been marvelling over, what the on-board guides have been urging us to protect. Sure, it's not reef fish that we are eating, but it is fish. It's hard to reconcile. Everyone eats them though, as it's hungry work being out here in these wild seas, looking at the wild fish. We load our plates, we come back for seconds.

We snorkel four parts of the reef, and they all are different. It's easy to think the sea is all the same, but from below there are distinct neighbourhoods. I keep making arrangements with Ellowyn to meet. 'Just there,' I say, pointing to a patch of water to the right of the boat. 'When you get in and have your mask and snorkel working, I will meet you just there.'

Billy will have nothing to do with a sea meet-up. He wants to be alone. He pretends there is no one else on the boat but him. Ellowyn tries, but we can never find each other. 'Just there' is a very hard place to meet when everything looks the same.

We get back into town late and walk home in the dusk. The bats are out. They fly high up in a lazy flap, their wings silhouetted against the moon. I say, 'Kids, do you think men really landed on the moon? Do you really think the earth is round?'

Billy looks at me like I've gone crazy. 'Mum, didn't you

go to school? Didn't you go to science class?' he asks. 'Is this heat making you go mad?'

After our big day out on the reef we need a rest. All the kids want to do is lie on the sofa and watch TV. Which is what I bet everyone else is doing in their boarded-up houses. We take turns making dashes over to the supermarket for food and then spend the next five hours lying in the dark recovering. We eat, we breathe, we watch.

Big leaves drop. Big spiders spin big webs. Outside the bathroom window thick dry leaves lie on the ground. When a leaf falls out there it makes a loud thud. The leaves are big enough to hide a snake under. I know the snakes are here. I can feel them watching us, like the dogs do. We have to keep the bathroom window open. For ventilation, the sign says. I wonder how open.

There are 27 steps from the front door of our apartment to the swimming pool, but we can't make it. It's too hot. Instead, we pull all the beds out into the lounge and we lie on them all day.

There are three of us, yet somehow we have 10 devices. We fight for the one plug to charge us into the cyber world. The plug is behind the red chair. Swift, secretive swapping goes on behind that chair. If you aren't charged, your only choice is to watch TV. We are all exhausted with TV. Evangelicalism is so stressful it makes my left eye twitch.

Shane calls. He wants to go out for a drink, so we meet down by the city pool. Surprisingly he orders a beer. 'Hey, what about that no passion thing?' I ask.

He shuffles a bit and replies, 'Yeah, I've been thinking about that, I'm thinking I might need a rest from having no passion.'

In the pool mothers cuddle their babies, boyfriends cuddle their girlfriends; the air is loaded with intimacy. Shane talks of detachment and not wanting to get involved, of directing all his love to God, but also of his desperate loneliness.

I admire his honesty. Not many would admit to being in love with God and also being lonely. But I really don't know what to say. I think of all the things I love: my kids, my land, my friends, I even love my clothes. I think how sad I would be without all of that. Maybe it is okay, to be living in my spiritual hole.

Shane says, 'It's my guru, though, I can't let my guru down, he's in charge of my soul and has agreed to save me.' He hunches over, puts his head in his hands and rocks back and forth.

I say, 'Oh, Shane, haven't you seen *Sex Lives of Gurus*? It's on Netflix.'

He jerks his head up, goes red and starts to push the plates around and bangs the sugar. He clumps in his chair. 'Jokes,' I say, feeling mean. But it's true. There's enough scandal there for a TV series for sure.

I say, 'You know what, Shane, you've bought into this idea that we have all done something bad, and that's why we are here, but what if we've all done something good, and that's why we are here. What if it's a massive treat to be on earth?'

Shane stares at me, incredulous. 'No,' he says, 'you're just making things up now.'

I feel Shane's despair; it's hard to know what to do in this life, it's hard to know if anyone has any answers at all. But I know I need to look after my own self, and this is a holiday after all. The beginning of everything new. It's not time to be stuck inside, or in theological whirlpools.

So the next morning, before the heat rises I walk the three blocks to the car rental agency. It's time to go and see the Daintree Rainforest. Kathy, a local girl, works in this office. 'Born and bred here,' she says, 'so I can give you the best advice.'

We fill out the forms together and I tell her where we are driving to. She stands up, leans over her desk and looks hard at me. 'Do not get out of the car,' she says. 'Do not go swimming, do not go paddling – fresh water or the sea. Do not even walk on the pavement. Look from the car. Do not get out of the car. It's the crocs. They're real, they're deadly and they'll get ya.'

The newspapers say the same thing. There are crocodiles everywhere. They are farmed for the tourist parks and during the rainy season their babies float out over the barriers and increase the wild population.

There are reports of people walking along beaches and crocodiles rushing out of the sea to grab them. When the friend in front looks behind there is no one there. There has been a stealthy, quick drag. Their friend is gone.

We pack the car full of things so we don't have to get out, even if we get stuck, and drive up the highway. There are cliffs and trees on one side and white sand beaches on the other. It's postcard perfect but we don't stop; we look from the car.

At Daintree Village, all the car parks are empty. It's just us in town today. Billy won't get out. He has taken to heart what Kathy told us. He keeps the window wound up and watches us as we cross the road.

Ellowyn loves shopping so we go into the only shop
there is. She makes a straight line for the locked jewellery
cabinet. I hear a shocked gasp. 'Mum, Mum, look at this,'
she breathes. She points to the bracelets sitting on the dusty
shelves. They are made of toad skin. 'I don't understand.
How can this be jewellery, Mum?' she asks. She points to the
dark melanomas on their skin, 'Who knew toads could get
sunburnt too?'

The shop doesn't sell much else. There are small bottles
of water for five dollars and pamphlets advertising crocodile
farms. Luckily we already have water in the car. Luckily we
already have nice sparkling jewellery.

Ellowyn takes some pamphlets, though; she likes bright
things to look at. But these advertise awful things. Teasing,
taunting things. She looks at a picture of a crocodile trainer
with his arm in a crocodile's mouth. Then she puts all the
pamphlets on the back seat, out of sight.

For it's scary enough just looking at the river out the
window. It is wide, swift and full. It looks like everything
deadly in the world lives in it, holding its own against the
current. We cross it on the car ferry, its engine revving
against the churning water. Billy insists he sees a water snake,
Ellowyn covers her eyes with her fists.

On the other side the National Park starts. Trees
overhang, the rain comes and goes, moss drips, epiphytes
spill over tree trunks. Cassowaries wander slowly across the
road, their blue neck feathers gleaming in the low light.

We stop at a boardwalk, nudge the car between fat tree
trunks and get out to walk. The sides of the boardwalk are
completely fenced. No hopping off and, more importantly,
no hopping on. Big movement happens up in the canopy.

Birds screech. Sometimes there is a crash, sometimes something thuds, something slithers.

But down on the forest floor, down where we are, it is silent and intense. Trees grow out of the water, their trunks buttressed with air-breathing roots. There is so much concentration going into the growing of things that the focused sound is of silence. We try to walk quietly, to make it as if we aren't even there. Ferns curl up out of the ground, they spill out of forked trees. Insects crawl. A bright blue butterfly spins by.

The boardwalk circles us back around to the car park. Silently we get back in the car. Billy lies down in the back seat, closes his eyes and seems to be breathing quite a lot. Ellowyn puts her head in her knees, locking her arms around herself. And I drive on.

We pass picture-perfect beaches, some with people on them. It's time for lunch, so taking a big breath, and trying not to remember too hard the warnings, I suggest a picnic on the beach. 'Not swimming, not paddling,' I say, 'just a picnic. Not going into the forest, the river or the sea, just sitting in the middle of the sand.'

There is a little track from the car park to the beach. At the beginning of the track there is a vinegar station. The sign says to put vinegar on if you get a jellyfish sting, as it will ease the pain during the drive to the hospital. 'No paddling,' I say again to the kids.

The beach is a tiny strip of white against the flat sea. It's perfect scenery, if seen from the car, or from a coffee table book. Seen from a picnic rug it is more unnerving. It's sticky hot, but no one will move into the shade.

'Snakes in those trees,' says Billy.

No one wants to sit down either. 'Harder to run when you're down,' says Ellowyn. So I share the food into cupped hands and we walk down the beach.

Ellowyn has this thing where she can't bear to hear people eat. So the only time we can have a good unselfconscious eat is when we wander off alone. That's what we do. 'But not too alone,' I call, 'I need to be able to see you.'

There are other people here, and we all seem to be in the same situation. They wander the beach, nervously keeping to the middle. I hear other languages, and I can tell by their clothes and cameras they are tourists. I don't see any locals. Everyone is unsure of what to do. We know we are in one of the most magical, beautiful places in the world. Somewhere untouched. Somewhere authentic, wild and real. And we are all scared.

We eat quickly and scramble back into the car. We get to Cape Tribulation before we know it. Indeed, we don't know it. Coming across three old buildings in the forest, I get out to ask how much further it is to the Cape. Apparently it is here. This is Cape Tribulation township. There is a public toilet, a general store and a café. We go into all three things, relishing this humanness. The general store has wide empty shelves. A few chocolate bars, a few cans of beans, some soap powder. All with hefty price tags. Luckily I have everything we need in the car.

We drive down to the actual cape, the actual beach. It is as before. Picture perfect. Trees everywhere, big bright green leaves hanging over white sand. No one wants to get out. Billy says, 'I think the rental car lady was right, it's much better to look from the car. I love this car.' So we sit and look. We marvel at the beauty, at the glorious world out there doing its dangerous thing.

We are all grateful we have this protective tin capsule and our little apartment to go home to. When we pull up outside, our street doesn't look so hostile any more. I even call out to the neighbour's dog, 'Hey there boy, it's only us, we're home!' He barks like he wants to kill us. They all do.

The rain thunders on the roof all night. I think of all that forest out there, just out there, and how much it must love this rain. I think of all those creatures, slithering and crawling and clambering over the wetness. I can feel the forest growing from my bed.

In the morning it's all over. The sun is out again, but the air is clear and cool and it makes you want to do things. Shane calls. He says, 'There is a party tonight, do you want to come?'

I think about that. I'm getting pretty tired of Shane and his weird ideas. At first they were funny and I felt okay about laughing, but now they just feel sad. He does seem to be very unhappy, behind his insistence of bliss. But an Aussie party in someone's backyard does sound fun, and I'm still on the lookout for Mr Right. So I say okay.

Finding the party is no problem; it is the only place in the street with an open gate and the only place with music pouring out. I broaden my accent a lot, in an effort to fit in, and I say 'Mate,' and 'Good on ya,' when someone pours me a drink. And it's good fun. Sofas have been dragged out into the back garden and some fairy lights twisted around the bottom of the palm tree. Someone has blown up a kids' paddling pool and some girls are standing around in it.

All the men are gathered around the BBQ drinking and

joking. It looks a lot like home. And there is Shane. I haven't seen him for a while, and he looks different. He has on normal clothes, he hasn't shaved his head and he has a beer in his hand.

I tell him about the Daintree and how it felt to be in such a wild place where everything is happening all at once. He says, 'It's Mum's bingo night. She loves going and seeing all her friends. She won't be home till really late. Really late.'

The bats are out again, flapping away up there, circling the town, looking for food. I go over to the BBQ and join the talk on sport. I don't know much about sport, but I fit in if I just say, 'Yeah.' And it's fun, just to be with some different people on this hot Australian night. It does feel like I'm hanging out with my neighbours.

Shane hovers. I figure he wants to talk, so we go and sit on a sofa. He keeps fidgeting with his beer bottle and he keeps looking at his watch. I ask how the religious thing is going for him. He leans in, really close and whispers, 'I'm not being a Hare Krishna any more. The truth is, since I've found Krishna I've become hornier than ever.'

I lean away and say a little nervously, 'There's nothing wrong with sex, nothing wrong with some passion, you should get out more, you know, try stuff.'

Shane puts his hand on my arm and says, 'Yeah, but do you want to come back to Mum's place with me? Now? Before bingo finishes? Please?'

The girls in the paddling pool really are getting quite drunk and the party is getting quite wild. I figure it's not my place to sort things out here. I'm not interested in sorting things out at Mum's place either. It's hard to let him down, though, this confused lonely man. 'Hey,' I say, 'there are plenty of fine women in this town, I'm just passing through. Best to find someone that's going to stick around, you know.'

I walk home down the middle of the silent streets. I can feel the dogs watching and the snakes, the spiders, and everything else here that creeps and crawls. Suddenly I am glad to be leaving here. Even though I know that it means leaving my kids. Leaving my precious, lovely kids. Leaving them to find their own way in a world full of confusion and weirdness and loneliness. While I try to find mine.

At the airport I hold them tight. As tight as they will allow, as long as they will allow. Which isn't much. They say, 'See ya, Mum,' and walk through the departure gate. Ellowyn turns to wave.

Shane sends me a text, 'I'm being a Hare Krishna again,' he says.

# THREE

# The Meditator

IT HAS BEEN HARD TO UNTIE MYSELF FROM MY LIFE. I've cleaned the house, put my stuff in storage, and rented it out for a year. I've packed up work. The time in Cairns was the final family holiday. So now is my big moment. I'm free.

And I'm really tired. I have tried hard not to let Billy and Ellowyn see how tired I really am, but now they are not here it starts to swamp me. My eye twitches, my heart races when I lie down in the evenings. Often it's hard to breathe. Often I don't feel anything at all. I worry about that; I don't think it's good to be numb inside.

I've heard that Bali is a place for healing. There are classes on yoga, meditation, tantra, reiki, tai chi, chakra realignment, aura cleansing, chanting, ecstatic dance, qi gong, sound baths. I don't know what most of those things are, but my friends have assured me there will be something there that will help.

I also know Bali has fireflies in the soft evenings and

black butterflies that stop on red hibiscus. Stories tell of water temples, rice paddies and gentle people.

I rent a room in a family guest house in Ubud, the town at the centre of this wellness industry. My room is a wooden tree-hut, high above the garden. I am at eye level with clumps of brown coconuts and look down onto the backs of butterflies and tree ferns. On the far bank, rice paddies gleam yellow through the trees.

My hut has its own verandah, where the thatch roof hangs low. It looks like a perfect place to sit and watch the wind. I know instantly that if all I do here is sit out there my healing journey will start. It's easy to sleep here too; the fan swishes me off in an instant.

I wake late to the sound of someone humming and a broom brushing the path below me. I clunk open the wooden doors, lean over the verandah and look up the river. There are squirrels in the trees, white birds above, the wind is warm.

In search of breakfast, I go out into the jumble of lanes. Every second shop is a café, so I don't have to go far. Pink flowers spill over door frames, vines twist up verandahs, gamelan music plunks quietly. I lean back with my coffee and enjoy the warm air.

Other tourists stroll by, enjoying the peace of this early morning. A young woman waves out to me as if she knows me so I wave back. She pushes her sunglasses up, stares at me, then hurries over. She slips into the spare chair at my table. 'I'm Emma,' she says, twisting her hair around her neck, then bending down to give me a hug. She unpacks her shoulder bag and lays out her things on the table: a phone, organic tea, a dream journal, a white crystal, a pendulum, three white feathers.

Emma has rings on every finger and bracelets jangle up her arms. She can't stop talking, she can't stop rearranging. When I start to speak she rushes in with, 'You are such a special soul, to hold space for me, I see your golden aura.'

Emma wants to tell me everything. My simple, 'Hey, how are you?' has opened her whole world. She is staying in the eco-organic health spa further down the lane.

'I've run away for a bit,' she says. 'They won't let me eat pizza down there.'

Emma tells me of her law career, her loving family, her expensive education and her despair. At first I think she is making things up, but then I see how her hands shake, and she actually cannot stop talking. The more she talks the faster she talks. She becomes unintelligible after a while. I put my hand on her arm and say, 'I have to get to the bank before it closes.'

'Yes,' she says, 'I have to go too, I've got an aura cleansing to get back to.'

There are lots of us here it seems, the eye twitchers, the ones with racing hearts.

If I go left down the lane, I get to the rice paddies. If I go right, I get to the main road. My lane mediates the chaos and the serenity. I do need to go to the bank so I turn right and head into the chaos.

Cars built for different roads, wide roads, overhang the centre line and choke up both lanes. Motor scooters weave through, laden with people talking on their phones. Traffic officers stand on the sides, blow their whistles and wave their hands but nothing changes. I stand beside one, hoping for some help to cross the road, but there is no help to be had here.

There is little help for pedestrians anywhere. The paths are one thin person wide and they are crowded with women selling fans, fruit, concert tickets, and sarongs. Men sit on the side and yell, 'Taxi, taxi.' Bewildered, hot tourists carry umbrellas for the sun and jam up the footpaths.

A man calls to me, 'Hey, hey lady, I saw you in my dream last night.' I smile and shake my head, but a connection has been made and he is quick to follow through. He stands up, offers his hand to shake, 'Kadek,' he says. 'I love people from New Zealand, I will wait here for you with my taxi every day. If you need me, I am always here.'

One of the money machines is in an air-conditioned booth. I lean against the wall, my heart racing. I take big gulps of cool air and let my sweat dry, before facing the chaos of the walk back.

At home I sit on my verandah and watch the night fall. White birds fly high above, coming home from their day's fishing, tiny swifts dash between the trees. When I lean over my rail I see the blue backs of kingfishers as they dive into the river gully.

I sit there, high above everything and feel free. Fireflies make squiggles in the dark. One comes and lands on my towel. Geckos call from my roof, there are rustlings, whooshing and the garden becomes alive with things I cannot see.

The next morning I start my hunt for some healing. There are lots of things to choose from, but I choose the first yoga studio I come to. My only criterion is the time. I'm not getting up early to get to a class. None of that rising early and rushing around business for me any more.

The class at 1pm is called restorative yoga. That sounds perfect for me. I have a list of things I want to restore. I put my mat down in the back corner, best to be out of sight while this restoration happens, I think. I lie down on my back and close my eyes while everyone else comes in. Best not to see. Besides, the only way to stop my eye twitching is to close them.

The room fills up and it's a hard class, but I sort of manage, especially if I don't look around much. I concentrate on the instructions and my own breathing, and I try not to notice that every single person in the room is wearing tight Lycra.

I really don't know how the ancient spiritual practices of yoga came to be associated with tight Lycra. I am the only one without any, and I feel it, in this class of the super cool, the super spiritual, the super stretchy.

After class I look through the yoga shop attached to the studio. I look to see if there are any accessories I could get myself for tomorrow to help me fit in a bit more. There are Lycra pants and Lycra bras in all sorts of mystical, spiritual, nature-loving patterns. They come in one size only, extra small.

There is a huge array of prayer beads. There is incense, soap, mat spray, massage oils. Really, there is nothing to help me fit in here at all. I think I must have the wrong sort of body for this yoga studio.

The yoga café seems to be the place where everyone hangs out between classes. I order some 'Green Goodness' which the label says is 'Fresh. Slow. Cold Pressed.

Organically Inspired.' And I wonder what the difference is between organically inspired and not organic.

I take my Green Goodness over to my organically inspired lacquered table. Maybe that's how we get away with the Lycra pants, maybe they are organically inspired too.

The café has long benches, encouraging communal eating, which is nice. I sit down on the end, next to Rachel and opposite Dani. They are both here on a three-week yoga retreat, and they fit in perfectly. They are young, very thin and have very long hair. They pull it out of their high ponytails and shake it down their backs. They have visible stomach muscles below their Lycra bras.

The girls have two weeks left to go on their retreat and are up to the shopping bit. Dani excuses herself quickly. 'Sorry, but I have to go,' she says with a quick smile, 'I'm off to the market to get some Buddha heads, much cheaper here than home.'

I ask Rachel if she is a Buddhist too. 'Oh no,' she says, 'Lakshmi is my Goddess.' She leaves as well. 'Meditation,' she says. So I drink my Green Goodness, and look at the hangings on the walls. 'We are all one,' they assert, and 'You have the universe inside you.'

On my way home I see Kadek on the opposite side of the road. He stands up and yells over the traffic, 'Kiwi girl! Hi, Kiwi girl!' I give him a wave and he holds up his Taxi sign. I shake my head and he yells, 'Tomorrow! Kiwi girl!'

Emma is there too, sitting at the front table of the café, eating pizza. She wants to tell me that nothing is working out for her. She cries. She has started journaling and wants to read it to me. She tells me I am an angel, and my golden aura is brighter than yesterday. She tells me the people at the health spa are mean to her and I am her only friend. She cries more. She talks and talks, and I cannot get away.

Even though I am on my own here, it's actually hard to be alone. Solitude is one of the things I know I need to heal myself. One of the big problems of being a teacher is there are too many people, too many relationships you have to have. I work out that I have taught more than two thousand teenagers. That many people makes for a numb inside after a while.

In the evenings, the pool at the guest house is unlit and I can swim alone in secret. I sit on the edge and dangle my legs in the black water, then I slip in and float on my back. The stars and the frogs are very good company. On my way back a thin black snake presses against the shady side of the stairs.

I hunt for other ways out of my lane, ways that I don't have to pass Emma or Kadek. I go left towards the rice paddies, and there I find a tiny footpath winding down the side of a temple wall. It feels massively secret. Banyan trees overhang, their aerial roots brush through my hair, and the gods watch from over the crumbling wall.

I go fast down this lane, though, for these banyan trees grow quickly and their roots are already touching the ground in some places. I worry they might grow around me if I linger. There is a statue in the temple grounds that has been encased by their roots. I can see half a shocked white stone face; the rest is all roots. I fear I could end up like that too. Absorbed back into the tree.

The market is in the middle of town, its narrow alleyways crowded with art, clothes and jewellery. The stallholders watch my eyes, to see if they rest on anything, if my pace slows. Then they bunch around me, a sarong is pushed in my face, 'You want?' Someone yells, 'I have big sizes, lady over here.'

I slip into a little café, tucked away in the middle of the market, and order fried rice. From here I can watch market life. Tourists walk down the middle of the lane in the sun, ill at ease, big and sweaty. It's easy to spot the wellness seekers, they wear their Lycra even to the market. I see Rachel, from my restorative class. I wave and she comes over to show me her shopping. She has 10 organic bamboo singlets with hoods, some orange prayer beads, and 25 silk scarves.

She is going to a chanting class and invites me too. 'Chanting makes you one with the universe,' she says. I am a bit wary, after Shane and his chanting, but it seems the universe is sending me those who chant.

We are a bit early, so we sit in the garden to wait. I lean my sweaty back against a banana palm. It's cool and I can feel the water in its fleshy trunk. Orange flowers, birds of paradise brush against my thighs.

Rachel goes over to her friends and they all sit cross-legged on their chairs. They talk of unlocking their DNA. Of ascension. Of raising their vibration. Of healing the world. Of finding bliss. Of expanding their consciousness. Of waking their Divine Feminine.

At the base of the banana palm there is a little green frog. She is the same lime green as the tree. I can see her breathing. Her skin moves in and out on the sides of her back and under her throat.

Above, the clouds are gathering, there are black smudges at the edge of the horizon. This is the wet season, the time of afternoon thunderstorms and flooding rivers. This is the season for the frogs.

The chanting is in a big wooden building with open sides. It feels like a bigger version of my tree hut. We all sit on the floor, cross-legged, eyes closed. One of the boys starts an 'Om', no one joins in so he stops after a bit, and then shuffles to the back. Someone does a high-pitched giggle, but mostly we are silent, serious, eyes closed, preparing to join ourselves with the universe.

The musicians sit down at the front and the chanting starts. Everyone sings really loudly; they sway and clap. I think of Shane. I think he would be happier in a place like this, where you still get to chant but you don't have to obey all those rules. It would be hard to end up in despair if you chanted like this.

The afternoon rains come while we sing. Outside becomes a stream of silver. The frogs enter into their full-force croak while the rain streams off the thatch and pounds on fat leaves. We sing the names of God over and over, calling out together, while nature streams and pounds and rises.

This communal singing does bind us. I look around kindly at all these people and after an hour of singing together I love them all. The universe is inside us. We are all one.

I walk home in the rain. It's so hot that it doesn't matter that I have no umbrella. The rain hammers down on me and I can barely keep my eyes open through its force. But I watch the path closely, as these are dangerous times on this broken footpath, for now a river gushes underneath. One wrong move and I could lose myself completely.

The traffic stands still. Bucketloads of rain tip down. I take off my shoes, roll up my pants and wade up my lane.

Kadek is sitting under the overhang of a shop and yells, 'Kiwi girl, taxi, taxi!' but I am enjoying myself in this rain.

I call back, 'Tomorrow, definitely tomorrow.'

Kadek is waiting outside my guest house in the morning, full of smiles, his car well-polished. We stop at the coffee plantation on the hill up behind Ubud. We sit, looking out over the rice fields and up to the mountains with our coffee. He shows me pictures of his family, his wife and three children who live in the village an hour's drive away. I show him pictures of Billy and Ellowyn.

He tells me times are hard for him. He doesn't want to drive a taxi, he wants to make wood carvings. I sympathise, I know how it feels to not want to go to work. We talk about art, and how hard it is to get the time to do that. We drink coffee side by side on a wooden bench under a thatched open-sided hut. His leg gets closer and closer to mine, and I don't think it's an accident when it touches.

Kadek is taking me to Lake Batur, a crater lake of Mount Batur. The road snakes up and down the mountain, rich green terraces stepping down its sides. Fish farms line the lake edge. So do advertisements for sunrise walking tours to the summit. 'Sunrise is an auspicious time,' Kadek tells me. 'It is to start again, fresh. It is time for something new.'

On the drive back Kadek tells me he is very unhappy. Not only does he have to drive a taxi, but his wife doesn't like him any more. He would like to start again, fresh. He wants something new. With me.

He tells me he has a great idea; he has been thinking about it all morning. 'You can open a shop in New Zealand and sell my carvings, then you can come back, bring me my money, and we can have sex. A lot of sex.'

I am quiet for a bit, for that is quite some proposal, then I ask him how many others he has asked. He sighs and says, 'Many, I don't understand why they say no. Tourists love my carvings and they love sex; they do in all the movies. I am not unattractive. People tell me I have movie-star eyes.'

I feel for Kadek. It does seem unfair that life does not turn out like a movie, even when you've got the eyes for it. But I say, 'I'm not interested in that Kadek. I think you should try working things out with your wife.'

He drops me back at the end of my lane in the middle of a traffic jam. He is despondent and silent. The black clouds are gathering, there is thunder in the distance and I know the afternoon storm is coming.

At home, I sit under the deep eaves of my roof and watch the rain. Up here, life feels spacious and free. But I know the living here is dense; this is a highly populated island. To the visitor this looks like paradise, but like anywhere there are rules and complications that bind. The sky turns the same black as the roofs of the houses. Sheets of rain fall. The storm is intense, but I ride it, free.

Emma comes searching for me. She wants to take me out to lunch, to her favourite restaurant where they make the best fries. It is down the end of our lane, out in the rice paddies. The local stallholders call out to us as we pass, but Emma is talking so much we don't hear.

She tells me about her aura cleansing, what her therapist says, about some sound healing she has done, what is in her dreams, what channels the coming eclipse will open.

She nervously ties up her hair, then unties it again. She pushes her sunglasses up, takes them off, chews the ends. We have to hurry and bend our heads when we pass her health spa. 'I'm not supposed to be out,' she whispers, 'I'm supposed to be in silence. And completely organic.'

We walk on raised earth paths through quiet rice paddies. Smoke rises from the burning of the chaff. It is all yellow and green and still out here as the rice pushes through the mud. Chimes clink in the breeze, playing music to the rice goddess.

The café is right in the middle of the paddies. Emma lays out her things on the table again. She opens her journaling book and writes lists as she talks. She underlines things, circles things, and tears well in her eyes.

Even though she has brought me here for the fries she can't decide what to order. She cries some more. I don't know how to help Emma, but I listen and I look out at the yellow rice and the black clouds gathering overhead and I enjoy the goodness of just looking at that.

Emma picks up her pendulum and holds it over the menu. It spins for a minute then comes to rest on mango ice cream. 'That's what the universe is telling me I need.' She smiles through her tears and orders a large bowl.

The tree hut next to mine has been empty, but in the morning I find I have a new neighbour. She sits meditating on her verandah in the early golden light. She has an orange shawl draped around her shoulders, her dark hair piled up in a knot. Her stillness pulls my attention.

At breakfast our eyes meet and I cannot look away. She shines with honesty, steadiness and something else, something else. Her name is Monique, she is from France. She invites herself to my table and tells me about her meditation master. And as we talk, angels sing, trumpets play and sparks of fairy dust fall around us. She comes here every year. She says, 'When you find what you are looking for, why go anywhere else?'

I don't want to go out now. I don't want to see Kadek pleading, holding up his taxi sign at the end of the lane. I don't want to listen to Emma and I don't want to be stuck in traffic. I want to sit up on my verandah watching the birds and I want to wait for Monique to wave out to me.

I think, here I have been looking for Mr Right, when maybe it's Ms Right that I should have been looking for all along.

Her eyes burn into me. I know she watches me as I walk to the pool and I know she waits for me to get up. She may be meditating but she manages to make breakfast with me every day even though I change the times I'm there. The air between our huts is charged, and we ride out the afternoon's lightning and thunder in sizzling tension.

Monique goes out every day at lunch to see her meditation master. I ask to come too, but she smiles and says, 'You must find your own path, not copy mine.' So I head on back to my restorative yoga with Dani and Rachel. I don't think my path is working though; nothing feels restored yet, but I like talking to the girls.

I tell Rachel and Dani about Kadek. They both laugh, 'You have no idea the number of proposals we have had here,' Dani says. 'Every day we get men wanting sex or business deals or both.' I tell them about my secret lane. Dani says, 'There are secret lanes all over Ubud. It's part of the charm of this place.'

I talk of Kadek, but I don't talk of Monique. She is too much of a secret charm to be talking about.

In the evenings she waves to me from her verandah, I

wave back from mine, and we sit and watch the night fall.
The birds come home, the fireflies wiggle. We are metres
apart, yet I can feel her breathing.

At breakfast she asks me to go to a sound bath she's
going to, just for fun. I like fun. I think gleefully to myself,
'A date! a date!'

The class is in a high-up wooden room, open to the
frangipani flowering. Everyone is lying down, so we do too,
on the edge, close to the flowers, close to each other. People
have brought blankets, eye patches, sleeping mats. I have
nothing, but Monique has brought a sarong for a blanket.
'You can share mine,' she whispers, and floats it above both
of us.

'Close your eyes,' the instructor says, 'and you will enter
into oneness with the universe and these celestial gongs.'

I close my eyes. The heavenly choirs are already ringing
through me, just lying down under a sarong this close to
Monique.

The room vibrates with sound and takes me along with
it. I become a gong, resonant, quivering, exultant. The only
thing that matters in the world is this trembling sound.
Time expands and all there is is gongs. The whole universe is
ringing and I am inside it all. And Monique's hand holds
mine.

This is what I want to do forever now. I think sound
baths are the best thing in the world. There is nothing more
healing or expansive or life changing than lying on the floor
and reverberating with gongs.

But Monique wants to go over to Lovina, on the
northern coast of Bali, to go snorkelling and dolphin
watching. I figure she has finished the meditating part of her

holiday and is up to the fun part now. With me. I like fun so I squish into a minibus with her and we head for the coast. We hold our packs on our knees and I feel like a real traveller. This is what I set out to do and here I am, a proper backpacker.

The road is tight and windy, the drive terrifying. We watch the jungle growing out the windows. Monkeys hang around on the side of the road, waiting for food scraps thrown from cars, the leftovers of picnics.

The bus stops for a rest break, but the driver tells us not to go far and to take a stick to beat the monkeys off. I don't think I will be very good at beating off monkeys. Monique certainly has the strength to do so, but not the inclination, so we both stay close to the side of the van.

It's a steep climb up the mountain, but going down is worse. A baby in the back seat vomits but there is nowhere to stop. We open the windows, and hot air rushes in. I want to scream; it is so hot and the smell is so bad we are all on the verge of vomiting. I lean my forehead on my pack and, second by second, I count until we reach the flat and the drive is over.

It feels different over here, the plains stretch out to the sea and it is wilder, rougher. Cafés crowd the lanes, motorbikes laze around, patrolling to see who is new in town.

We are stopped by Wayan who wants to take us out snorkelling tomorrow, then by Putu who also wants to. Putu also has a box of pearls under his arm. He opens it and spreads the pearls out on a cloth on the footpath for us to see. He tells us his brother went diving for these pearls.

Down at the sea a wooden pier heads out into the ocean.

Couples walk up and down with linked arms. We sit on the edge, feet dangling to the sea, and watch the light fade. To the west the huge volcanoes of Java rise cone-shaped out of the sea.

New adventures could happen here, new possibilities. A lot of people sit here, holding hands, looking at new horizons. One of the boys has brought a guitar; he sings, 'Darling, you look wonderful tonight,' to his sweetheart. And all the rest of us sing it in our hearts too.

Wayan's dolphin trip is packed with tourists in the morning. Nobody minds, though; we all want to get out and up close, we are itching to get started. Monique and I roll up our pants and climb into the back seat of the wooden outrigger. Ours is painted blue and white and called *James Bond*. There are boats on either side of us and they are filling up too. Suddenly this dolphin watching thing feels like a race. Agitation rises, 'Quick, quick, quick,' Wyan urges us. Boats pour off the beach.

*James Bond* gets up to speed and we race out with the others. The dolphins are here, lots of them breaking the water with their fins, jumping then disappearing to come up a long way off. The boats race and chase. Everyone wants the perfect picture and we all become part of a dolphin hunt.

Then suddenly everyone wants a touch. It's not enough to just see dolphins, we want a touch. People lean over, they make clicking sounds and dangle their hands down, desperate for a close encounter.

Then it is all over. The dolphins turn and head out to sea, the boats turn for the beach. We slump in our seats, wet from sea spray, exhausted from the hunt, dazed by the oneness.

I go back to bed; Monique goes out shopping. I turn the fan on high, close the curtains and pretend it's still dark. I am in the delicious half-asleep state when Monique comes home. She flops on the bed next to me. 'I'm so tired of proposals,' she says. 'Two men just now proposed sex and business deals. Please don't propose anything, Sarah. You are my beautiful interlude. No proposals.'

So it seems this is not going to be Ms Monique Right. I sigh a little, but I know she is right. Sometimes interludes are the nicest things of all. I am happy with this interlude. After all, I have the whole year stretching out in front of me and France is not on my list.

The Menjangan marine reserve is the place to go snorkelling. Monique has never been snorkelling and has saved the last few days of her time here for this. It's a hot two-hour drive on the bus to get there. The boom and bust of tourism has happened fast here. Old resorts crumble back into the jungle. Vines clamber, trees crowd in clumps and coconut palms rise above it all.

The boat is small and old but it works. The boys who run the trip are in a good mood. The sea has become part of them; I can tell by the way they fall silent and just look out to the horizon, the way they joke with each other and toss equipment around.

They know their way around under the water as well. Wayan snorkels with me for a while. He catches my hand and steers me over to a patch of sea anemone. He dives down, shakes its filaments and out comes a clown fish. He comes to the surface, we splutter off our snorkels and he yells, 'I found you Nemo!'

There are people on this trip who can't swim. They are

given life jackets and floatation noodles and then tied to a long rope. It's as if they are pegged to a clothesline and then let out to sea. They dip their heads in for a little bit, not trusting the snorkel but using the mask, bobbing about in shallow water. When it is lunchtime Wayan hauls the rope in and they all come along with it.

Luckily Monique is a good swimmer. We snorkel together, holding hands. I am very careful to hold the right girl's hand this time. The current is quite strong, and even though the shore is near and definitely swimmable, we snorkel close to the boat. We hover over the coral, holding on to each other and this moment.

Our last day together is at the Banjar hot springs. It seems strange to be going to hot springs in such a hot climate, but when we get there it makes sense. The water is only warm, the same as the air, and it is bright green, the colour of a jewelled gecko. The pools are long and narrow and water fountains from the mouths of stone dragons.

We talk of our homes. Monique is catching the bus straight to the airport tomorrow, and my plane ticket is for the day after. She says, 'I come every year Sarah, I come for meditation, for teaching. Maybe next year I will see you.'

I say, 'I don't come every year Monique. I may not see you.'

So we sit quietly in the pools, and she lays her head on my shoulder, and under the green water our ankles are linked.

It's nice getting back to Ubud, to my tree hut, but I don't unpack because I have an early-morning flight. I go out into the lane for tea. Kadek sits at the bottom of the lane, waiting for someone to hire his taxi and someone to make him rich and happy. Emma is sitting in the pizza café, crying and writing in her wellness journal. She has all her talismans spread around her.

I slip into a little café alone and sit at the back, in the shadows of the garden. There is music, incense, and statues. Ferns grow at my feet, orchids flower on the table, geckos run the ceilings, frogs croak in the pond.

I look around at all this beauty and think about staying here. I could keep renting out my house and just stay here. And when Monique comes back to her meditation master next year, she could also come back to me. I wonder how that would be, the waiting thing. How it would feel to stay here and join in the endless healing and wait for Monique. There are a lot of people living here, trying to find their divine goddess, trying to tune their chakras. I could become one of the permanent seekers.

Inside me, though, I know that the busy yoga classes, the celestial gongs, the chantings have not eased my heart. They haven't touched the stinging shame, the bitterness or the emptiness that I carry. Nor has the brief time with Monique. This time in Ubud has been a veneer of healing, not the real thing. If I stayed, I would continue to layer the veneer. I need something else.

The northern hemisphere is still shivering in the midst of winter, but the sun always shines on the Costa del Sol. So I have bought a ticket to Spain. I'm going to see what happens when I don't try to heal myself with classes. When I just fill my days with nothing but the sun and the sea.

I hear him first, loud from the front of the café, 'I'm Mike, from Australia,' he booms to the waitress. Mike wants everyone to hear him. I put my head down, rummage through my bag and find my book, my eating alone prop. Mike sees me and shouts, 'Where are you from?'

I look at him over the top of my glasses, 'New Zealand,' I say and go back to my book.

There is a long, long silence, then, 'Mike, from Western Australia,' he yells. He stands and walks to my table, holding out his hand, 'A Kiwi, are ya?' I know Mike is looking for love, and I know he thinks I would be perfect. He will not be put off.

I finish quickly, pay and leave. It is nice to be out in the soft dark, and I walk home thinking about a night swim. A motorbike roars behind me, I stop to let it pass, but it is Mike, revving his engine next to me. Big and loud, Mike from Australia. 'My grandad was a Kiwi, ya know. West Coast. Don't know how the buggers survived. Bloody hard land.' His belly meets the handlebars, he fills all the space. 'Want to come for a ride on my bike? I still know how to give a lady a good time.'

I don't like rides on bikes. I don't like big, loud Mike, but he follows me on his bike until I turn off into my guest house. Those Aussies with Kiwi grandads do not give up easily.

A night swim is the best thing to do on my last evening here. I float in the dark and look at the stars and think about the proposals for love, money, business, all the searching for wellness. Clean out your chakras, find you bliss, fire your divine spark, change your life.

Everyone is looking for their lucky charm here, and the magic of Bali makes us all think we can find it. If we can just stay long enough, just make that next class, that next sunrise. That next organically inspired pizza.

# FOUR

# The Minotaur

IT WILL BE FUN, I THINK, TO LIVE WITH A SPANISH family for a while, to be part of something but also separate. To have the vitality of children around, but not to be responsible for them. Carmen and Antonio advertise their spare room for rent. Their house is one street back from the beach along the coast from Malaga. It's right in the heart of the tourist mecca but seeing I'm a tourist myself that holiday-spot vibe could be just what I'm looking for.

I am so tired when I arrive, I barely have time to look around before I am asleep. I sleep all day; it's been a long flight and I'm jet-lagged. Antonio is delighted with me when I wake in the evening. He claps his hands together and yells, 'You are already Spanish, Sarah! You already know how to sleep all day! You will fit in with us perfectly!'

I sit out in the garden with the family and eat dinner. Carmen has cooked a feast to welcome me and the table is loaded with frittata, polenta, cheese, olives. The curly-haired kids wiggle around and are soon on my lap, their arms around my neck, pressing in close.

Antonio is the only one who speaks fluent English. This doesn't deter the others, though; everyone shouts at me and assumes I understand, and strangely I sort of do. We sit up late, drinking wine in the soft night air. The neighbour's orange tree is in full blossom and I take big breaths of it. I can see breathing deeply is going to become my favourite thing to do here.

That, and embracing family life for a while. I cuddle little Alfie on my lap while Maria plays with my hair. I pass around photos of Billy and Ellowyn. Antonio shouts, 'These kids look just like me Sarah! These kids are my kids too!'

Billy and Ellowyn look nothing like Antonio. He is short and bulky. His dark hair curls all over him; it tufts out his shirt sleeves and neck. He is handsome and commanding and he looks nothing like my kids. Carmen looks at the photos and nods, 'Si, just like us, these are our kids too.'

The next morning Antonio leaves with a bang at 5am. He is back at 8am to take the kids to school in a flurry of shouting. I am pleased it's not just me that has to yell at kids to get them in the car. I get up and wave them off. They look too small to go to school; their bags are almost bigger than they are.

Carmen leaves at 9, she has a job in a shop down on the main road. She tells me everyone will be home for lunch soon. She shows me where the beach umbrella is, leaves me a key, kisses me on both cheeks, then leaves in a rush, slamming the front door, the garden gate, the car door.

I pick up the beach umbrella and walk down to the generous bulk of the sandy beach. I see why this coastline calls to the weary and the sun starved. Huge mountains rise purple behind us, putting the stress and pressure of Europe at our backs. It feels like this strip of beachy land between the mountains and the sea is our own little country where rules don't apply. Only happiness applies.

There are cafés down on the beach. Mostly they are empty for it is the off season, but still they have outside fires lit in old metal dinghies. Coals smoulder red and the heat rises in a shimmery haze. Wood smoke drifts and the day stretches out into forever. I eat charred kebabs for lunch, sitting on the sand and looking out to the sea.

My gaze rests on the horizon line, and I feel the pull of Africa, just there over the edge. I know Amadou will be there soon. Even though he lives in Melbourne he spends half of the year in Guinea, his homeland. And even though our relationship is off at the moment, it always has the potential to be on. It's the way it has been over the years; really, it's just the long-distance thing that has made the relationship impossible.

I am so close and the sea looks so flat that if I stretch my arm long enough, I could touch the top of Africa. I could get there easily, it's so close. It would be fun to visit Amadou in his own land, to play music, to dance, to just be with my old friend, my old lover.

In my mind I reach my way down the west coast to Guinea. I feel what it would be like to go there next, and my heart races. In a good way. I file that feeling at the back of my heart and head and concentrate on what is in front of me. The green, green sea.

I walk into it for a swim and it's as if I'm walking into the sun as well. It hovers over the horizon and glints a sea path for me. And it is just for me. There is no one else in the water at all. Everyone else lies on sun loungers looking exhausted. Antonio is right, to sleep all day is the normal thing to do here.

My whole day is spent at the beach. I read, look to the horizon, think about Amadou, read a bit more. I look to the mountains, think about Monique up there, not that far away, in the rush of Paris.

And I think about Ellowyn. I don't think she is doing very well. It's hard to get her to pick up her phone, to answer anything. When I do speak to her, she cries. She has had big fights with her friends; her flat isn't working out. I think about meeting her somewhere, and a holiday to look forward to would help pull her through this tricky time. But it's hard to know what to do, when I'm this far away.

When I go home everyone is asleep. It's 4 in the afternoon and the sun is still high in the sky. I lie down on the sofa and fall asleep too, lulled by the quiet enchantment of the sleeping house. I wake to the sound of the TV; the kids are watching cartoons at my feet. Carmen and Antonio look indulgently at me; they are delighted with this public sleep. 'You belong with us now,' Antonio says.

Carmen claps and beams and puts her hands on her hips. 'Si, you are us,' she says.

The kids think so too. They have no qualms about jumping on me and shouting, 'Hola Sarah!' I do their English homework with them while we watch TV. They are completely bewildered by English, and as I try to teach them, I become bewildered too. It seems like an incomprehensible language with impossible rules. But the next day their school books come back with big red ticks and A grades. I am proud of myself.

I spend the first week down at the beach. I paddle the tide line and look to the mountains. I swim out into the sun. I lie on the sand and breathe in the wood smoke.

The next week a brand-new awning gets installed on the side of the house. Antonio tells me they can afford it because of the money I am paying for my room. 'So this is yours too, it is because of you we can all have this,' he exclaims generously.

The awning is striped yellow and white and takes up half the garden. It is just like a cheerful tent and everyone loves it. Carmen drags out the old sofa and the kids jump up and down on it and yell, 'Gracias, Sarah. Gracias.' I am astonished at how I can appear to be so generous, how this is all turned around and I am the one who arrives bearing gifts.

Carmen brings home a tumble of plants in terracotta pots: ladder ferns, pink bougainvillea, and lilies. We arrange them around the edges and suddenly we have a lush forest in the tent. Antonio comes home with an orange tree. He lifts the tiles outside, in the corner next to the door. He calls over Maria and they plant the tree together. 'Now we have everything,' Antonio says, 'an orange tree, and all this space for our family,' he sweeps his hand wide to include us all.

Everyone loves the tent so much that we start living out there. Every day more things appear. The kids pull out all the cushions from the house and make secret huts among the pot plants. Antonio moves the speakers out and Carmen and I move out the dining table. Carmen is happy, she pushes back her long hair and twists it over her shoulder, hands on hips to look around the tent. 'Perfecto,' she says, 'this will be a place of good times.'

The city of Malaga is close enough for day trips and there is a bus stop just past our house. I walk down, wave out to the bus and climb on. I press my face to the window and watch the shops and high rises stream by. In the next block of shops a bakery with its windows full of pastry flashes by. I realise it's walkable. Definitely walkable, and worth a day's outing soon. I grin to myself.

Apartment blocks jostle and cram into tiny spaces all the way into town. I don't think there are any planning regulations here at all. Even the high crumbling cliffs are built on. It looks like the buildings have been flung up in a panic and all the coastal towns have merged into one giant mash-up. Little striped awnings hang high in the air off the edge of all the apartments. I can see why Antonio and Carmen are so delighted with theirs.

Looking at all this I feel lucky that my family is out of town. They have a whole house, single storey, with a tiled backyard. There is plenty of room for kids to run and chase and shout. Plenty of room for a striped awning, a pizza oven, an orange tree. Over our back fence is a market garden. Strawberries and tomatoes grow there, just out of the tourist gaze. Antonio and Carmen made a good choice when shopping for their house.

I get off the bus in the middle of the town square. The shiny tiles reflect the sun and suddenly it's unbearably hot. High palms tower above but they are not enough to absorb the glare or heat.

It's too hot for the town so I walk through the gardens and head for the castle. Bright parrots fly low. I buy a paper twist of roast almonds and sit for a while to eat and watch the parrots. They fly down the wide pedestrian paths, squawking and flashing their colours. They nest in the heads of the palm trees, and it feels like I'm in the middle of a tropical forest here in this city.

The castle is at the end of the gardens, up a steep hill. It's still hot but solid old trees shade the paths all the way. Surprisingly I find myself alone on these paths. I wander up, keeping to the side in the deep shade. At the top of the hill the castle rises high and the city stretches out to the sea, glaring white in the sun.

I sit on the ramparts, legs dangling and look down to the bullfighting ring below me in its yellow circle of dust. Further out is the sea. The port is filled with a fleet of chunky white cruise ships, choking the harbour even though it's still the off-season. They are bigger than any invading force of the past, for sure. Every morning an army of tourists walks up this hill to take selfies and shout over the parapets. Every evening they walk back again. This castle can't hold off the waves of tourists on those ships.

I understand why they come, though. It's easy to feel like you're in the past here. The old city is full of narrow alleys and intrigue and time moves slowly. It feels like a young man could still play music at his sweetheart's window, that a fan would not be out of place, or a flouncy dress. Flowers fall slowly from trees, sensual love hangs in the air. Alleys widen out into squares with outdoor cafés. Everyone sits and has lunch with friends and life is slow and good.

My own days start to revolve around lunch. I get up early, go for a swim, read for a bit then settle in for a long lunch. It's wonderful to have a huge platter of food to nibble for hours and then to have an afternoon sleep. I can feel myself getting well here, I can feel the numb parts of me thawing out.

I pay a lot of attention to food and how it's cooked. Definitely there are different tastes to lunch cooked over the outside fires on the beach than lunch cooked with electricity. I imagine making a permanent fire pit in my back garden in New Zealand so I can cook like this all summer for the rest of my life.

At home I talk of the loveliness of the sea, just down there, almost in front of the gate. 'We prefer the nudist beach, Sarah!' Antonio shouts, 'to swim without clothes is the only way! We will take you in the car Sarah, and we can all swim with no clothes on! It is good for you, the salt in the water, it is good for your skin to get that!'

And, indeed, it is good for the skin to be naked in the water. It is a completely different feeling, a wild, free, sacred feeling. The whole family comes, and everyone is naked and it is completely normal and wonderful. The kids run and shout on the edge of the sea while the adults lie in the sun. After a while I don't see why all beaches aren't nudist beaches. I think this is exactly how I'm going to swim for the rest of my life.

Spain is changing me. Soon I won't want a house at all. I will be happy living forever in a tent. Cooking on an open fire. Naked.

All this rich food and all this lying around at the beach needs to be balanced out, so I decide it's time to start exercising. Antonio tells me there is exercise equipment in the garage. In the evening he comes out with me to show me how to use it. He starts the running machine and gets on, he turns the music up high and says, 'We will do this together. I also must exercise.' So he runs while I use the rowing machine. We keep turning the music up. 'Motivation,' Antonio shouts above it. It's like we have our own nightclub going on out in the garage.

After two songs we are both exhausted. He leans over his machine and wheezes, 'This is good, this will help me. Sarah, I cannot be the man I want to be in the bedroom, not with this stomach.'

I laugh, and say, 'It is impossible to resist the glory of Spanish food.'

He declares he will exercise with me every night. 'We will get our stomachs down Sarah! We will be all we want to be in the bedroom!' he shouts.

Carmen refuses to exercise. She says she has enough running around after the kids and Antonio. She is right: she does run a lot and she looks very fit and strong. In the morning she ties her hair up, and starts her day of child carrying, door slamming, grocery hauling. I know how strong that makes a woman. She pats Antonio's stomach and rolls her eyes at me and laughs. Antonio laughs too, and grabs her hand, he pushes it against his stomach. 'This will all be gone!' he shouts, 'and very soon, now we are exercising!'

Antonio tells me he has a job in town in an office and that he works normal hours. I have no idea what these could be. Sometimes he leaves with a bang at 5am, sometimes 11, sometimes he stays home all day. His hours are completely unpredictable. Friends come and go at all hours.

This is a very sociable house, there are always extras for dinner, they stay up, drinking late into the night and appear bleary-eyed sometime the next day, looking for their car keys. I can't keep up with who is who. Their Spanish is loud and fast, and I don't understand anything.

I explore the back streets and I find a public park behind some apartment blocks. It's a good place to lie on the grass and it makes a nice change from the beach. There is exercise equipment too and lots of people come and use it. People throw sticks for their dogs, kids ride on their trikes. Old people do tai chi, and slow dances with fans. They bring out old CD players and practise their routines on the footpath.

I lie under a tree with bright orange flowers, read my book and watch all this life, and it feels like I'm a part of it too. It's easy to belong here, easy to sink into this slow life and feel a connection.

I increase my exercise to include splashing down the tide line to the next town. I want to find the bakery that I saw from the bus. I dawdle, looking down at the sand for shells and up to the mountains for inspiration.

The bakery sells fruit tarts, egg pastries and cakes. 'Got to try the local delicacies,' I murmur to myself, 'no harm, now I'm exercising.' I buy a strawberry tart, sit outside and eat it slowly in the sun, my eyes closed to the deliciousness of the moment.

On my way back I meet Sandy, a retiree from Manchester. She is also splashing in the tide line, her skirt tucked into her pants, her long grey hair matted with salt and wind. She says, 'This is my second life, my real life. The other one seems like a dream now.'

We walk back down the beach, back to the bakery and I have another strawberry tart with Sandy. She is worried about Brexit and what that will mean for her. 'I can't go back there, to the cold, to the anger, I can't,' she whispers. 'Neither can my friends,' she sweeps her arm to include all those dozing on their sun loungers, the army of retirees.

Most of the people on the beach are retirees. The summer holidays haven't started yet so these people are the lucky ones, living their second life here in the sun. This beach life makes up for everything. The angry bosses, the cold cities, demanding children, crowded buses, grey skies. All the injustices of their first life drift away. All that matters now is the sea, the sun and the smell of wood smoke.

Sandy has a tiny apartment up on the cliff behind us. 'It's just a place to store my things,' she says, 'really I live down here under these umbrellas now.'

She invites me back to her umbrella and says I can pop by any time, though she may be asleep. 'The best sleeping is down here on the beach, in the middle of the day. That's the healthiest. To sleep in the sun, with the sea, the smell of a wood fire, that's the best sleep to be had in the whole world.'

Out in the garage in the evenings, on the exercise machines, Antonio talks about his family, and how hard family life is. It seems even in this paradise there are problems. We talk about children and family expectations, about money and responsibilities. We talk about how those demands make a person tired, poor, unhappy.

'But now,' he exclaims, 'I have turned all the hard things around, Sarah! Yes, I have done that. I have a second life now. Carmen and I have become swingers, Sarah! We have become happy! Yes, we have become happy.'

I am so surprised I don't say anything for a bit, then I smile and say, 'Good on you.'

'Yes,' he shouts, 'we even have orgies, Sarah! This is why I must get my stomach down. My life will be even better with a stomach that doesn't get in the way!'

I realise that all the comings and goings may be for reasons other than work. I smile, remembering how my offer to babysit the kids last week was met with elation, how they both stayed out all night. I think of all the friends looking for their car keys in the mornings. Suddenly a lot of things in this household start making sense.

Sandy sends me a message. She wants to go into Malaga for the day with me and offers to show me around. 'I'm almost a local, local enough to have my heart here,' she says. We meet at her umbrella, stop by the pastry shop for morning tea, then catch the bus into town. We walk the narrow alleys, stopping in little cafés. We wander around grand churches and watch buskers in the squares. It's nice to have a friend who is almost a local.

In the afternoon, we visit the Picasso gallery. Picasso was born here in Malaga and this city is proud of their boy. Sandy tells me, 'You can see the Malaga light in everything. It never left him. For his whole life he painted with the light of Malaga in his hands.'

The gallery is full of tourists and we quickly lose each other, but I don't mind. I prefer looking around galleries by myself. And this art startles me. I walk around with my heart thumping, my eyes feasting. It feels like Picasso is actually here; his art shouts out his life force. I stop and look at 'The Three Graces' for a long time. It makes me feel startled and breathless, those three women standing there, half naked, their bold sensuality taking up the whole wall.

I move on slowly. I stop at a painting of a minotaur rescuing a woman in a boat. The minotaur is really a bull-man. He oozes masculinity and sex. His hair curls everywhere, he is naked, authoritative, pleasure seeking. This art seems too shocking, too intimate for a public gallery.

I feel my face going red, and it's hard to look away. Further down the corridor there are lots of pictures of dark curly-haired bull-men with women, naked women. It all seems erotic and dangerous and intimate. And when I look closer, all the art seems like that. It seems that sex is everywhere in this gallery.

I find Sandy and we catch the bus home. I get off at her stop too, and we stop by the bakery, then I walk her back to her umbrella. 'It's a good life here,' she says. 'I have everything I want. You could do worse than to stay here too.' I tell her about my plans. To go to Guinea with Amadou, to meet Ellowyn somewhere.

She warns me off, though. 'You have to be careful out there in the world, it's dangerous out there.' She talks of terrorists, plane crashes, wild animals, diseases, thieves. She tells me to stay. That here it is safe.

I say, 'But here you have thieves, plane crashes, diseases, wild animals. You also have bulls, Sandy, do you have to be careful of those?'

She looks at me straight in the eye, 'They are the worst,' she says, her hands on her hips, 'whatever you do, do not get tangled up with a bull.'

When I come home Antonio is lounging on the sofa in the awning. He has no shirt on, his dark hair curls all over his chest and down his arms. He pours me a glass of strawberry juice and asks which Picasso moved me the most. I say, 'The Three Graces,' even though it is not that painting but the one of the naked minotaur.

But he loves 'The Three Graces'. He says, 'I like them too, I like naked women. I like naked women more than anything.'

I sit down and drink my pink strawberry juice. Seagulls call into the evening air, smoke drifts up from the beach fires. He continues, 'I cannot live without sex, Sarah. It is my drug. I have sex with a lot of women and what I have found is that they are all looking for a prince. But there are no princes. There are only animals and animals want to have sex. I love my wife and my children, and I am not going to run away and leave them. But we are all animals, Sarah.'

Carmen brings wine out. She brushes against my arm and gives me a slow lovely smile. The neighbour's orange tree makes the air sweet. I breathe deeply, filling myself with orange blossom and strawberry juice.

Antonio takes a deep drink of his juice. He says, 'Would you like to join us in a threesome, Sarah? Maybe an orgy, Sarah?

'We have everything here, Sarah, we have wine, juice, coffee, we have music and speakers, we have shade. And we have many friends.' He leans back and smiles a generous smile. 'Life is very good right here.'

I laugh a little, I say, 'I will think about it.'

He laughs too. 'If you are ever ready, we are here,' he says.

I can see now that this awning is almost a harem tent. It wouldn't take much. Some thick carpets, generous pillows, a billowing door, some low lamps, and this would be a harem tent. A pleasure tent. I realise all the apartment blocks in this town have awnings. Everyone has a covered balcony, a tent off to the side of their house. I wonder at the use of their awnings. Is this whole town filled with pleasure tents?

And now sex is always in the air, the offer of the orgy is now always in the air. Suddenly everything becomes sensual. The way my skirt moves when I walk. A look over the shoulder. The half closing of a door. Big breaths of orange blossom. An afternoon sleep on the sofa.

These hot days call for lying around in the shade, drinking strawberry juice, listening to slow pulsing music. These hot days do call for lots of friends.

I start to look more closely at the friends that come around. There are some lovely friends, there are some not so lovely. I wonder who is in the orgy friend group. Is it all of them? It is impossible to tell, and it is impossible to ask. I think about talking to Carmen, finding out her take on it all, but it's hard. She doesn't have enough English and I don't have enough Spanish to start a conversation on orgies.

Seeing as I am in the south of Spain, there are some places I know I need to visit. Also, I need a break from the family and some time away from all the sensuality. Granada is close, so I will go there for a few days. It will be nice to be on my own again, free and unnoticeable.

The bus speeds through the plains to the north of the city and it feels like I'm galloping on a horse with a cloak flying out behind me. Granada glows in the morning light. The Alhambra, the palace, rises up in pink turrets against slabs of snow high up on the Sierra Nevadas.

I stay in the old town. There are alleyways, squares, churches and built into it all is the intrigue of love. The place is full of suggestions, of secret alliances, of a flowing robe disappearing round a corner, of private gardens, private fountains, and private rooms.

Tiny alleys lead off hidden squares. They are filled with Moroccan shops selling soft slippers, silk curtains, candle holders. And here it is again, the forcefield of Africa shimmering out there just over the mountains.

I spend the whole day at the Alhambra. So it seems, does everyone else in the world. The entranceway is packed with high buses. But the Alhambra is so magical, so well designed, that the tour groups dissolve away. For this is intimate architecture; this palace is designed for sensuality, for secret rendezvous, for love.

High up, from the deep shade of marble arches, I look across the white town. To be this high up, to catch the wind and look over town from a shaded balcony, is a fine, fine thing. Down there, buildings crowd in on each other. People like living close to each other in this country it seems. So close there is only room for skinny trees between neighbours.

In the palace gardens there are courtyards planted with loquat trees and lilacs. I walk through orange groves, lavender fields, I sit under cypress trees and eat my lunch. Surprisingly there are a lot of New Zealand plants here. I find a cabbage tree, and my eyes prick. Something from home. A great treasure from home. I sit down, put my arm around it and lay my cheek against its rough trunk. I sit there for a long, long time.

In the evening I sit on the church steps and watch buskers in the square. Musicians play, dancers stamp and lift their skirts. There are red flowers in dark hair, there are men in black tight clothes. The fight is in the dance, there is dust, blood, sweat, boldness. There is Triumph.

Driving back over the hills, the silhouette of a giant black bull looms. It is part of an advertising campaign from the 1950s that was so popular that it became public art. People love their bulls down here and the bigger the better. The statue is so startling, so true and so ridiculous that I laugh. It seems I am home, back with the bulls.

I get off the bus into a storm growling away over the ocean, coming up from Africa. The wind blows sand sideways into my face. I think of sandstorms in the desert just over there and people running to their tent. Shielding my head with my arm, I hurry to our tent.

Everyone is there, eating dinner. The sky is black and rain splats on the top of the awning. Antonio lights the outside lamps and we eat in the storm. The kids love it. With wide eyes they wiggle and burrow into the sofa and scream at the lightning.

When the kids have gone to bed, late, in the dark, Carmen and I eat loquats. We slowly peel the skin off, slowly suck the yellow flesh off the seeds. We sit side by side on the sofa, arms touching, feet up on the small table with the bowl of loquats between us. Rain patters on the canvas and it's warm and close inside the tent.

Antonio brings out a massive watermelon and cuts into it. Neither of us wants watermelon; we are content with loquats. But Antonio wants it, and he wants us to have it too. He passes us over a huge slice each, giving us a huge smile. We all eat, juice dripping down our chins, our hands. I get to the white rind and put it down on the plate.

Antonio says, 'No, no, eat more, you must eat the white.'

I pull a face and say, 'I'm done, Antonio.'

He leans over and shows me his phone. He has found a page about watermelon. He reads it out, 'The white of the watermelon, next to the rind, is a natural Viagra.'

I say, 'You seem to know a lot about sex, Antonio.'

'Yes, Sarah, I know a lot about sex, Sarah, it is my hobby. I am always researching my hobby, Sarah.'

Carmen rolls her eyes at me and stands up to fold the washing. I offer her my white watermelon rind. She laughs, pushes it away. She offers me her watermelon rind. Both of us laugh a lot. Carmen throws an arm around my shoulder and kisses my cheek. Antonio is very pleased.

The rain gets heavier, it pelts against the canvas awning, and the hot wind pushes the sides in. It does seem that the best thing in the world right now would be to camp out here in the tent and relish the storm. I don't, though. I head to my room. The loquats have made me sleepy. The watermelon rind hasn't worked, maybe it takes more time, or maybe I didn't eat enough of it. Antonio yells after me, 'Sleep well, Sarah, we will be out here tonight if you want us.'

The next time Antonio and I exercise out in the garage he asks me if I think his stomach is getting smaller. He pulls his shirt tight across it and says, 'Be honest.'

I look from a few angles then say, 'Yes, yes, I think it is.' I don't really think it is getting smaller, but that is of no consequence because he is charming and generous and funny. I would be surprised if any lover complained about his stomach.

He sighs and says, 'Not enough. This stomach is still getting in the way, Sarah. And my back hurts. So I cannot give 100 per cent in the bedroom. I must keep exercising.'

We talk of other things that could help; I suggest eating less, drinking less, but he is astonished I could even think that. 'Impossible!' he shouts. 'There must be something else.'

I talk about other things that help bad backs. I suggest yoga, tai chi, maybe joining one of the classes down at the park. Or celestial gongs. I know for a fact they induce magic. They could tune up his back at the same time.

He loves this suggestion. He yells, 'I will buy some gongs and we will all lie down and have magic together! We will ask all our friends!'

The thing is I know he would be a good lover, even with a big stomach and a bad back. I know Carmen would be too. I know this because they are attentive and genuine and because between us all a quivering fire is building.

Besides, he has cannabis oil. 'This will work wonders when applied to certain parts,' he whispers.

On Sunday I go with the family to church. They keep asking me and I decide it's good to do some family things with them besides eating and sleeping. As soon as we sit down the kids start to fidget and turn around. Carmen tells them to sit next to me, 'They will be better behaved with you,' she whispers. They are not. They giggle and poke the shoulders of the old man in front. They kick at ankles and squirm.

But, still, it's just like being with Billy and Ellowyn. I imagine them here, sitting either side of Carmen, misbehaving. Billy likes to sing very loudly and off key when he's out in public. I imagine Carmen nudging him, hissing at him to behave himself. And I think maybe our kids do really all belong to all of us.

The church is huge with high ceilings and lots of air. It feels like a place where you need to take big breaths just to use up some of that air. The service is all in Spanish so I understand little, except that church is the same the world over. We stand, kneel, and sit. The organ booms out and we all sing songs of universal love. The kids squeeze my hands, they lean their heads against my arms and it feels good.

There are a lot of friends here at church. I recognise some of them from home, and there are some I have helped to find their car keys on some busy mornings. We smile and give cheeks double kisses, press arms and murmur into ears.

On my last day here I visit Sandy at her beach umbrella. I bring oranges and strawberry tarts to share, but she is asleep. I sit at the next-door umbrella and eat two oranges. I look out to sea. I lie down and wait for a bit in case she wakes up. But she doesn't and I'm not disturbing her best sleep in the world, not even to say goodbye. I leave the other two oranges and the tart beside her in the shade and write her a note in the sand.

The beach is starting to get busy now the tourists have started arriving, real ones not just retirees. White rows of sunbeds have taken over so I go to the park for the afternoon. I lie on the grass and watch the clouds smudge over the mountains.

It becomes hard to tell what is cloud and what is mountain. There are soft green prickle heads under me and I know soon it will be impossible to lie or walk on this grass. But, for now, I am blessed. There is a tai chi class going on and the music hangs in the air. I lie under my tree with its orange flowers and now and then one falls on me with a heavy thud. I watch the clouds. Antonio and Sandy are right, life is good here.

I think of that Picasso painting, the wild bull one in the town gallery, and my face flushes again. I remember the indolent pleasure of the bull, the intimacy of it all, the shockingness of it all. I remember staring at it for a long time, and the security guard staring at me staring at the painting.

I think of living with no rules, of living however I want. I think of having a free heart, one that does not grasp and hold, one that plays instead. I think of wild exuberant bulls, of passion, of flamenco.

At home the kids are having a sleepover at their auntie's. Carmen has lit the candles in the tent. There are thick rugs and pillows on the floor. There is a vase of orange blossoms. There is music. There is cannabis oil. There is watermelon.

# FIVE

## The Superstar

### GUINEA

AT THE LAST MINUTE MY FLIGHT TO AFRICA changes. I am now scheduled to arrive in Guinea first, at 3am. Amadou is flying from Melbourne and arrives four hours later. I call him from the airport. His excitable, fast conversation speaks of disaster. 'No one dares go out at night,' he shouts, 'that is the time of bad, bad things, unspeakable things!' He is not sure if his brother can pick me up at that time. He tells me not to get in a taxi by myself. He tells me to cancel my flight, to get something else.

I google Conakry airport. It is described as the worst in the world. There are travel warnings on the New Zealand embassy website. Do not go out at night. Carry your papers at all times. Stay away from crowds. Stay away from the police. Stay away from borders. The country is corrupt. Volatile. Liable to coups, riots, violence. There is no infrastructure. There will be no help.

I fly anyway. When we land in Conakry at 3am everyone claps, but I don't. Landing is the easy part. I'm sure there is far worse to come. Customs spills me straight out onto the street, and my plan of hanging out in the airport until the daytime is over. There are no street lights, no moonlight and it's really, really dark.

A low voice calls, 'Sarah, Sarah,' and I just trust that this is Ousman, Amadou's brother. I give a little wave and move over to him. He holds my hand. He whispers, 'Change money, change money for the taxi, for some food.'

The money changers are outside, on the other side of the wire fence. I can't see them, but I feel their hands grasping through the holes in the wire. I pass some US dollars through and get a fistful of crumbly Guinea francs back. It's hot and it's really dark. I can't see anyone or anything.

Ousman holds my hand and leads me to our taxi. It's an old Datsun. It's hard to breathe, it's so hot and I'm quite scared. My heart is racing, both eyes are twitching.

The taxi is full, there are six men already sitting there, silently. Ousman whispers, 'These are our friends. We need a lot of friends with us at night.' I squash in the back seat. It's even hotter in the car. I am handed a handle to wind the window down with. We pass the handle around. There is only one.

It's a bumpy drive to Ousman's house. The earthen streets are deserted this early in the morning. We have to walk the last bit, when the street turns into a narrow footpath. I can't see what I'm walking on, but I know it's rough and quite wet. By the smell I know the wetness is not from the rain.

I sleep for most of the next day. When I wake Ousman tells me Amadou has missed his connection in Paris. I am on my own with his family for a few days. None of us understands much about the other. I spend a lot of time sitting on a plastic chair outside. I watch big lizards with bright blue back spikes run along the walls. I carry water. I help light the fire. I stir the pot.

I try to speak, but my lessons in Susu evaporate in the heat and white light. A lot of visitors come to look me over. They bring presents: a mango, a coconut. We sit and look at each other and everything is strange.

When Amadou arrives there is jubilation, and not just from me. Amadou is happy to be home, and extra happy that I am here too. He says, 'Now we are on again. We should stop the off thing, and always be on. Forever.' I like the sound of that too. My heart races in the right way. I realise how much I missed him when we were off.

That evening a stream of musicians winds through the garden carrying big wooden instruments. They line up in the shade of the wall and plastic stools are rushed out for Amadou and me to sit on. It is loud, joyous music, with drums, bells and balafons. All the lyrics seem to be about Amadou. They sing his name over and over.

I begin to wonder if I really know who this man is. Our time commuting between Melbourne and Dunedin hasn't prepared me for any of this. More people come running into the garden. Women dressed in bright skirts and tops with head wraps tied in big bows, men in singlets and jeans. People have heard the drums calling, the word has spread that Amadou is home. They flick off their shoes and dance in the dust.

Amadou nods towards the djembe. The djembe player willingly hands his drum over. Amadou straddles it on the ground and begins to play. His hands move so fast they are just a blur. He cracks the air open with sound.

Sweat runs down his face, his body gleams. He throws his head back, flicks his dreadlocks over his shoulder and plays faster and faster. The people cheer and laugh and dance. He is home.

The music goes on late into the night. When the musicians are so exhausted they can't play any more, they stop. They kneel on the ground in front of Amadou, their heads bowed, and ask for his blessing. He puts his shoulders back and holds himself very tall.

They ask for advice. He tells them, 'Life can be very hard. You must find something to love; love is all there is.' I watch all these people line up for blessings, for words of wisdom, and I realise I am here with a Superstar.

That night we sleep to the sound of drumming in the streets behind us. It doesn't stop. I ask about noise restrictions, mutter about people needing to sleep. Amadou is shocked. He asks, 'Why would you have restrictions on joy? This music is a joy! This is what I don't understand about your country, the restriction on joy. It is a gift to have the drums playing all night. You will soon see.'

We leave Ousman's house and move into Amadou's, which is still being built. Even so, many people have moved in. They have piled the rubble in corners, put sheets over the window gaps and plastic mats on the floor. More people arrive at the gate hoping for work, but the house is already full.

A room has been cleared for us on the third floor, but it is so hot in there we can barely breathe. We sweep rubble off the balcony, drag out our mattress, hang some solar lights and put up a mosquito net. We make a little paradise out there, where the wind can blow through.

The balcony looks out to the river at the bottom of the garden. It is swift, brown and deep. On the far bank there are mangroves and tall coconut palms. A big white heron stands on the bank, still and silent every morning while the sun rises over the river, deep red, a perfect orb. The morning is the best time for river gazing, before the sun washes everything into a haze.

Amadou has bought half the river as well it seems. The posts defining the property are way out there and half the garden is swamped at high tide. He has plans to fill in the swamped land and spends a lot of time throwing rocks in there to build it up. But, really, out the back is mostly mangrove swamp.

I worry about crocodiles. Amadou tells me not to worry. 'It's more about hippos here,' he says. I look up hippos. Turns out they kill more people than crocodiles. My plans for river swimming are over.

The house is unfinished. It has no plumbing, electricity, windows or doors. It already seems to be falling down, though it's still being built. The concrete walls have holes already, some have been plugged with newspaper. The concrete comes off the walls in little balls and crumbles in my hand. I worry about sleeping up so high, and the whole house crumbling away in the night. Is it best to be on the ground floor or the top floor during a crumble? I don't know.

I think a lot about that, on the hot slow nights, while the drums play and play and I struggle to find their joy. During the day the drums become background noise, but at night they dominate. Every single night. Amadou has no problem sleeping through them, a half-smile on his face as he relaxes into their rhythm in his sleep. But I lie in an irritated sweat. They are so loud, so incessant, so intrusive. My head pounds with noise and I can't sleep.

In the mornings we clean our teeth off the edge of the balcony; we spit into the garden and Amadou throws the empty water bottle off as well. It seems all the household rubbish is thrown off the balcony. In the back garden I wade through water bottles, used batteries, toothpaste tubes, razors, plastic bags. I find a big bag and pick some up, put it at the side of the house and ask what day collection day is.

No one knows what I am talking about. Amadou instructs the cook to get rid of the rubbish. The next morning, I see her wade through the swamp to the river and heave the big bags in. It's that or burn it, I am told. In the late afternoons there are fires on the hills opposite. The build-up of rubbish over there is so big that fires smoulder and flare at the end of a hot day.

My irritation with the night drumming builds and smoulders as well. I know there is nothing I can do except try to change myself. I know I need to embrace this music, so I decide to learn an instrument. It will be a nice bonding thing with Amadou anyway, even if it doesn't help with the noise at night.

The balafon, a type of wooden xylophone, is the instrument I choose. The only reason I choose it is because I don't have to tune it. I can't seem to hear when things are out of tune, so I think this is the perfect instrument for me. Amadou is delighted. He squeezes my hand and says, 'Please,

please be good at this.' He hires Abram, the best balafon player in Conakry, to teach me.

I have my first lesson up on the balcony, sitting on the edge of our mattress. Abram sits opposite me. Up here in the afternoons all that exists is a haze of heat. There are mountains I know, and trees, but they are all lost in the white light. I have to squint just to see Abram on the other side of the balafon.

Many people come to watch the first lesson. Little girls hang off my shoulders, their fingers in my hair pulling it into tiny plaits. People lie on my bed behind me, their feet pushing up against my back. Plastic chairs have been brought up for the old people to sit on and watch. It appears Abram and I are the afternoon's entertainment.

So the lesson starts. Abram plays the first three notes and asks me to copy. There is silence. All eyes are on me. I play the first note and it is wrong. There is a roar of laughter. I try again and it's wrong again. The audience laughs and laughs, they bend over with laughter, slapping each other's knees. The little girls giggle and pull my hair a bit harder. The boys in my bed squirm their feet on my back.

We try for an hour; Abram plays his notes and I try to copy. I hit more wrong notes than right ones and I can't follow any rhythm at all. More people are called up to watch and to laugh. They laugh so much they cry.

Amadou keeps himself busy in the garden during my lesson. He throws rocks into the swamp and pretends he doesn't hear.

Little boys find my writing books and start drawing superheroes and lightning bolts. Women pull out thermoses filled with rice and pass them around. People laugh and talk,

some in the corner start to sing, and everyone has a
wonderful time during my music lesson. Except for me.

'This is just an extraordinarily hard instrument,' I tell
myself. And 'I wish all these people would get out of my
bedroom.'

That night, in the dark, Amadou says, 'How can you be
so bad at this? I have never seen anyone so bad at this.' I sniff
into his shoulder and say I am trying hard. He tells me that
rhythm is always happening in the air, all the time, all
around us. When he plays, he just jumps into the rhythm
that is already there, singing in the air. 'Can't you hear it,
Sarah, or are you just being silly? Can't you hear the rhythm
that is all around us? What has happened to your ears?'

Obviously something bad has happened to my ears
because I can't hear. I can't even wrap my head around the
concept of the universe singing or operating in rhythm. He
says, 'Everyone is laughing at you because they can't believe
you can't hear. You are the worst they have ever seen. You
can't keep time even. That is unbelievable.'

I know I have a lot to learn here, but I can't bear another
lesson. It's too hard to be laughed at like that, so I tell Abram
I need a bit of time to practise. And that is true. But I can't
remember anything to practise.

I help with the cooking, even though I'm not very good
at that either. It appears I have very few worthwhile skills in
this community.

I am given the job of pounding. It looks like fun when
the other women do it. They sing and laugh together, and I
am delighted to be included. I think it may also help with my
rhythm. I should be able to join in and keep time with the
pounding. Maybe even join in the singing.

For the first few seconds it is fun, and I can keep up. Then I quickly fall out of time. I get bored, my hands hurt and I want to sit down.

The other women laugh loudly, calling to each other, and they point at me. And suddenly I don't see the point in pounding. I think of just going up to the shop to buy something for dinner, then eating it secretly behind the trees.

But I keep going, out of time, my thud gets slower and slower. When the food in my drum is mush and I think I'm finished the women throw more things in. A whole onion goes in, some fish bones. I think they are playing with me. An onion? Can't that be chopped and not pounded? And bones? They laugh more and insist this is the way things are done.

I hype myself up, telling myself that dinner is going to be amazing after all this work, and the blisters on my hands will be worth it once I taste it.

We cook on an open fire in the back garden. There is no point buying a stove for there is no electricity. Even the neighbours, who are connected to the network, have power outages every day. Usually just before meal times.

The fire is lit by melting a thin black plastic bag over small sticks. Plastic bags are the best fire starters I am told, especially the black ones. We save the black ones; they don't get thrown into the river.

I love the smell of smoke, and of food frying. But I think there is something wrong with my taste buds as well as my ears here. The others adore this food, but I pass mine back to the children, waiting in the darkness.

The fire is lit every morning and goes all day, for there are many people to feed. The house fills up more every day, with visitors and with those who just stay and sleep in the garden. All day women sit in their bright clothes, washing rice for the next meal. By the time one lot is cooked the next is ready to go on.

From the balcony above, the fire looks like a mandala. Long poles of wood are pushed into the fire at the centre. The kids skip over the poles, playing games, while the women gather around the fire in the middle. It pulls us all in, this mandala.

We sit around it in the evening and I listen to life happening here. When I listen closely, I can hear some rhythm in things. I discover the frogs croak in time. They start at 7 every night and croak in a rhythm for six counts, then have a rest for two. I tell Amadou this and he is pleased. 'Exactly,' he says, 'now you are starting to hear. Even the frogs can hear the rhythm of the universe.'

Presents start arriving from the village. Half a bag of peanuts and two sacks of coal one day, a live chicken the next. It goes to live under the stairs, its legs tied together until we eat it. They are good presents, useful presents.

Amadou loves his village, and it seems everyone in the city loves their village too, for there is much talk of life there. Amadou says, 'Things are slower there, people look out for each other, and there is no rubbish. I think you are more like a village woman than a city woman. You will like it there.'

We eat the bag of peanuts at the front of the house in the afternoon shade. It is a favourite place for the men. They like to sit here, make tea, and watch life go by. It takes a long time to make a cup of tea. There is a lot of pouring from a cup held high to a cup held low.

So we watch the pouring of tea, the goats wandering

from bush to bush, the kids playing. We eat peanuts and call out to the neighbours.

When we go in, we pick up all the peanut shells. 'These shells are unlucky in front of a house,' Amadou says. I wonder at all the rubbish there too; aren't old razors unlucky as well? Someone could seriously cut themselves on those, or the torch batteries leaching yellow ooze. I ask Amadou. He wants me to be honest, he says, he wants to know if I could live here. So I ask about the rubbish. He sighs and says, 'Things are different here.'

In the early mornings Amadou and I work in the garden together. We pull out weeds and pick up rubbish to prepare for planting some fruit trees. In the cool of the mornings we crouch down and dig holes and put the trees in together, both our hands touching around the tree's roots. We plant mangoes, avocados, coconuts, and jackfruit. I can see this garden growing fast into an oasis of green plenty and I can see happiness here.

In the afternoons I practise balafon. I try hard but I don't get much better. I still pull an audience; they run up the stairs, laughing before I even start playing. So I think the best thing to do is practise very quietly and secretly. I barely touch the keys at all, so no one hears, and no one laughs at me.

At the next lesson Abram is cross. 'You must play like a lion!' he says. 'Show me your lion spirit. Make the music roar. Be loud!' I try to be a lion, but the girls are back plaiting my hair, there is a baby asleep in my lap, an old woman is wheezing with laughter on my bed and I'm still not sure of the starting note.

After a while I start to see things clearer. I realise we are sort of living communally here. I find it hard to figure out who is family, who are friends and who are paid workers, but it seems none of those distinctions matter anyway.

It also seems that all my things are no longer my things. They are communal things. I see people wearing my clothes. At odd times of the day there are people I don't know sleeping in my bed. There are thousands of pictures on my phone that I didn't take and of people I don't know.

I stop talking about 'my' after a while. When I need a skirt, I find a sarong that is lying around. If I need an afternoon nap, I find a free mattress. My thinking starts to change. If I have a piece of bread, I halve it and give it away. It seems impossible to keep something to myself. And here it seems as if there is no other world.

I look at my pictures of New Zealand and they all seem bland. I can't remember the sharpness of my land. I can barely remember my own children. I know they are important, but it's hard to hold on to why that is.

I try to keep in contact with Ellowyn, but she answers her phone less and less, and she doesn't reply to emails. Before I left Spain, I arranged tickets to India for us both, but apart from that, it is easy to let her silence slide, for it seems like Guinea is all there is in the world.

Amadou decides to have a family party, to bring everyone together before the music camp starts and his students arrive. We have to go downtown to buy the sacks of rice. Even though we live very close it takes most of the day to get there.

Amadou tells me aid money was given to make the city road into a four-lane highway, but almost all of the money went missing. It's only one and a half lanes of washed-out, potholed earth now. Young kids slip through the jammed cars selling cigarettes, phone cards and water, their mouths trembling with tiredness.

Amadou used to have his own flock of goats in the village, but they all died when a chemical spray went wrong. It didn't fertilise everything, it killed everything. So he has no goats any more, but the village will sell us one for half price for the feast.

The goat arrives in the afternoon by motorbike. Its legs are strapped around the driver's waist, its head leaning over his right shoulder. It has been a big trip for the goat I am told: it started off tied on the top of a minivan and at the central bus station it got transferred to the bike. It is tethered to the rubbish heap and eats white plastic bags all afternoon.

At dusk Amadou kills it in the corner of the garden. He lays down banana leaves and says prayers and cuts its throat. The other men stand in a circle watching while we women are all over by the fire peeling potatoes. Its skin is pegged out against the wall to dry; it will make a fine djembe skin.

Alpha turns up for the family feast. He is Amadou's best friend, so he counts as family. He has a business suit on, and I realise he's not here for the feast but for an important business meeting. He keeps repeating my name and shaking my hand. It seems the business meeting is with me.

Amadou tells me his friend is full of wild get-rich-quick schemes, and tonight is no different. He wants me to buy a metal detector from home and ship it to him. He has seen people finding gold rings on the beaches in Australia on YouTube. He points up to the mountains rising high above the river. 'Up there is gold,' he says. 'When I find it, I will be rich and then I will pay you back for the metal detector.'

Those mountains are dangerous, there are all sorts of big multinational companies up there mining and there are stories of terrible things. This is a resource-rich country; it has gold, diamonds, bauxite, aluminium. But the people are poor. Alpha sees the wealth pouring out of his land, they all do, and he is getting desperate.

My foreign status turns me into a bank, a walking bank, and not just with Alpha. People turn up all the time with gifts for me, a mango or a coconut or a bag of charcoal and then ask me to pay their year's rent, their electricity bill, their children's school fees, their new shoes. They say they are hungry, and I know they are. They ask for my phone, my sunglasses, my bag.

It's overwhelming and it's horrible having to say no. I have already blown out my money by helping Amadou with his house. Amadou too is overwhelmed, more than I am. People turn up at the gate every day, pleading for his help.

He spends a lot of time praying. I know he is praying for good things for his people, for Allah's gaze to rest a while on their suffering and alleviate it. Some days he cries during his prayers, and some days his prayers are especially long. 'It's the only time I have to myself,' he says, 'people can't ask anything of me when I'm praying.'

His younger brother, also called Amadou, is 24. He wants to be a football star. He walks around in a white football uniform every day, hoping a scout will see him, a rich overseas scout. But this is a Conakry slum and there are no scouts here.

A family meeting is called to see how he could be a football star in Australia. Or New Zealand. Expectations are high, especially from his mother. If one son can be an international musician surely the other son can be an international soccer star? She turns to me. 'We need a wife for him,' she says, 'a wife who will make him a star.' I don't know any women who want to do this or could do this. I shake my head, keep my eyes down.

It is almost time for the music camp to start. We have another family meeting to decide jobs, and most importantly what to do with the money the camp will make. I am included in the meeting because I seem to be family now, and because Amadou says so.

There will be enough money to either put white tiles on the outside of the house, or to do the plumbing and connect the electricity. At the moment there is no water; it all has to be carried in from the well down the road. It's hard to have so many people in the house with no plumbing. I know the music students will struggle, and I know the women whose job it is to carry the water are struggling now.

Everyone speaks. There is a lot of support for the tiles. 'They will increase our importance, everyone will think this family is successful,' Amadou says. We have a family vote.

The tiles win, fourteen to one.

Sometimes things here are overwhelming. When that happens, I go and sit down by the river by myself. It's nice to look for hippos, to watch the white heron quietly fishing.

But others always join me. People I don't know, strangers from down the river. They stand close to me in groups, they are quiet and press in close. I ask Amadou what's going on and how I can get some solitude. 'They see you alone there and they feel sorry for you,' he says. 'For us, being alone is a terrible thing. No one wants to be alone, so they come and stand for you.'

The music camp starts and Amadou's students from Australia, China, Japan and Europe start to arrive. We go out to the airport to meet them. Amadou plays his djembe to welcome them. Others get pulled in by the music, singing starts, a dance-off happens in the car park.

It's an easy, joyful beginning for the new students. I see their eyes flicking around but coming to rest on the drums, on the joy of the music and the dance. Amadou tells me, 'Mine is a culture you need ears for, not just eyes, and when you have those ears, inside you explode with joy.'

Music lessons start in earnest now everyone is here. Most people are here for the djembe classes, which Amadou teaches twice a day. But there are also dance classes, balafon, kora and flute lessons.

The word has got out that I am a teacher too. People start arriving for English lessons. I don't want to do this, I'm so tired of teaching but Amadou says, 'If you have some knowledge, you share it. You should teach those who want to learn. That's what happens in my culture. We share.' So the people gather around and we chant 'Good morning.'

And now the night drumming comes from our house too. Amadou doesn't sleep much, as he's too busy drumming all night. But I manage some sleep. Sometimes I get a burst of joy in my dreams. When I tell Amadou he smiles and says, 'Now you are starting to hear properly, that joy is what happens when your ears really work.'

During the day local kids peer in through the open windows, their eyes fixed on Amadou's hands. He calls them in and sits them in front of him. 'I am a griot,' he explains, 'my job is to teach all who want to learn. These children are all ours. I must teach them.' The kids join in the lesson, playing on old tins or buckets, and my heart bursts at the generosity of this man.

They stay for lunch too, and he feeds these kids with rice and with music. He says, 'I cannot turn away hungry kids.' But some evenings, in the dark, he weeps, 'It is too hard, it is too much,' he cries, 'how can I feed my people when I earn nothing?'

He is right. There are so many people here and very few are paying. We are both losing weight, we are both hungry in the evenings. We eat less so more people can eat something. I start to join him in prayers. I don't have the money either; the only thing I can think of is an appeal to Allah.

Amadou has hired a colonel from the army as protection during the music camp. Last year he got held up at gunpoint here, and he well knows that a house full of foreigners draws attention. The colonel sleeps at the front door during the day and stands guard during the night. He has grenades tied around his belt, and a gun on each hip. He is a giant of a man and in his army uniform he looks terrifying.

I don't make it to morning drum class, as it's taking all my energy to practise balafon and get to dance class, so the colonel and I have breakfast together. The drums start as we stir the condensed milk into our coffee.

His body starts moving and then there we are, dancing to the drums on the front porch together. It becomes our morning routine. The neighbours call out and wave and the world doesn't seem scary at all. I am careful of the grenades, though. I don't want any accidental bumps. I dance at a distance.

At night we all gather around the fire. We sing, laugh

and tell stories. Most of us can't talk to most of us, but the music tells us more stories than we can absorb.

There is a girl at camp from Shanghai, who doesn't join us at the fire. I find her down by the river. She has spread out her rattan mat and is lying on her back, a sarong covering her as mosquito protection. She is crying, laughing and hugging herself. 'There are stars, Sarah, there are stars,' she whispers, 'they are real.'

I lie down next to her. We listen to the others singing and we look up at the dazzle of stars. 'This is the first time I have seen stars,' she whispers. 'I came here for the music, and I get the stars as well. These are two gifts for me.'

Amadou's friends come during the daytime; they come to hang out, to play music, to eat, and to have a sleep on the only comfortable mattress in the house. Our bed.

There is one especially handsome man. He wears a white singlet, white tight pants and white shoes. His muscles are extraordinary. He has a diamond embedded in each tooth. Everyone envies those teeth. He plays balafon and kora, and when he plays no one laughs but sigh and clap instead.

We always know when he is here, for there are no women in drum class then. They are all out in the garden watching those flashing teeth.

The music camp lasts a month. There are no spaces that are not filled by music. Rhythm is everywhere. And I think my heart changes, becoming something more than a heart. It decides it's not just an organ to pump blood. It decides its purpose is to join the rhythm of the universe. My own heart becomes the loudest drum of all, keeping me awake at nights with its beating.

I think other things change too: my bones shift, they

seem more like tuning instruments, or flutes. Now and then something big blows through me. Something spacious and breathtaking.

And I have no idea about anything.

I start to hear things other than the drums. Sometimes, in the high distance, I hear singing. The most beautiful singing in the universe. It is so strange and lovely that I know it is not human singing. I am too overwhelmed to speak of it. I become very quiet and I listen.

Amadou organises a trip to his village for the music students. It will be a long day, for the roads are so difficult. His mother brings out a colourful hair wrap for me, to stop the road dust getting into my hair. I am grateful, for there is no hot water for hair washing here. She creates an enormous colourful bow at the front of my head.

Amadou is pleased. 'I like seeing you wearing colourful things,' he says. 'That western clothing of yours is too dark and plain; you should wear lots of colour like our women do and fit in more.' He is right, people do love colour here, the women especially. All the colours are mixed up and they all work.

My grandma used to tell me that when I was racked by doubt about my fashion choice as a teenager. She would take me out in the garden, fling her arms wide and say, 'What colours here don't work together?'

I would say, 'Nothing, Grandma.'

'That's right, nothing,' she exclaimed. 'Nature puts all the colours together and so should you. Be glorious like the garden.' Grandma would love it here.

We hire four taxis and everyone jams in. It is a long drive, the roads are rough and there are many roadblocks. We have

to show our passports and our vaccination papers to
policemen with guns and hefty boots. They flick through all
the pages, taking their time.

One points his gun at Amadou and says, 'I want one of
your wives.' I look around our car; it has Amadou, the
driver, four Australian women and me all squashed in. I
don't know if it's a joke, I hope it is. Amadou speaks very
quickly in Susu and the gun is lowered. We are waved
through.

I ask, 'What did you say? Was that a joke?' He just
shrugs, but I notice his hands are trembling.

The village is nestled under wide spreading trees. There
is no rubbish, things are gentle and quiet. We have lunch on
a mat under a big mango tree and Amadou tells stories of his
childhood here.

Village children press themselves close; they hold my
hand and I am taken on a tour. They show me the swings
into the river, the rice fields, and the school. Amadou is
right. I feel much more at home here than in the city.

Amadou talks with the elders. He is mostly silent, his
head down. He comes over to me. 'My people want you to
see a special place, a magical place. They want to see if you
can see the magic,' he says, 'but it is important you don't
touch anything there, or you could be lost. Will you come?'

Amadou holds my hand and we walk with the village
elders into a cloud of butterflies. At the end of the track a
spring wells out of the ground. We stand there in silence
while the butterflies flicker around our heads.

Afterwards I was asked if I saw anything. 'No,' I say,
'only the butterflies and the water.' They sigh and shake
their heads.

But I heard something and I didn't want to tell anyone. I heard that singing again, that high beautiful singing, and it didn't seem so distant; it seemed to come from that water. It pulled at me so much that I wanted to get into the spring, to sink under the water, to be immersed in that sound. If Amadou wasn't holding my hand I would have.

There are so many things I don't understand here and so many things I don't have words to ask.

The camp finishes, the music students return home and there is just us again. And some hard questions. Amadou asks me to stay, to live here. He says he will leave Australia and teach djembe in Europe instead, and I can stay here and run a business.

He wants me to open a school. He says I can teach and make a good business. His family will help. One brother can drive the school bus, one can teach soccer, his sister can sew the uniforms, and his mother can write up the accounts.

He says, 'We can all work this together. You can teach us English and we can teach you how to listen to the universe.'

I don't know if those two things can happen together. I think that business may silence the rhythm of the universe. I think that could be our problem.

I tell him I don't want to build a school or a business. That there is no point being here if he is not here, if he is in Europe being a superstar and I am here alone. He sighs. 'You still don't get it: you are never alone here, there are all these people. You can become one of us.'

I talk of Billy and Ellowyn. He says, 'Sarah, your kids have left home, you will be sitting alone in an empty house.'

I ask him to come and live with me, in New Zealand.

He says, 'I think you are in love with your country most of all Sarah, not with me.'

And I think that may be true. But I also think it is true for him. He is also in love with his country and his people. Now I see what it's like here. I can that see all his work in Melbourne is for this. If he had the money, he would live here forever, for this is his home. This is where he wants to be most of all, and this is where I can't be.

'I think this means we are off again,' he says.

My heart breaks when I leave.

# SIX

# The Selfie

I FLY INTO GOA THREE DAYS BEFORE ELLOWYN does. It gives me time to have a big cry about Amadou. My time with him hasn't eased my heart problem at all.

It helps that everything is different here. It helps that once again I am on my own and that I have a job to do. I have to find somewhere for us to stay. Somewhere peaceful where Ellowyn and I can reconnect and I can ease back into being a mum.

I scuff around the dusty back lanes of Anjuna, looking for places to rent. Old bungalows hunch under the coconut palms, and the jungle pushes in against their plastered walls. I come across an old pink hut that has 'To Rent' plastered over its gate.

I wave and call through the iron grilles. An old man shuffles down and clangs open the gate. A howl of barking dogs erupts. We shake hands and Manuel shows me around his property.

Just inside the gates, guarding the steps to the pink hut,

is a life-size statue of the Virgin Mary. She is encased in a stone grotto and seems to guard the place, along with the dogs. The garden is full of mango trees, and jasmine winds up through the ironwork. Inside the hut green glass windows stain the light, making the room into a quiet chapel. It feels perfect. We shake on the deal and I move straight in.

I spend the next three days crying out on the verandah. Mary watches from her grotto. Her head bowed, her glass door filling with condensation. Manuel watches too, from his verandah up at the big house. He waves to me whenever I look up.

It's good to have Ellowyn coming. It gives me something else to think about, to worry about. When she gets on her flight out of New Zealand, I walk down to the local café to use their Wi-Fi to talk her through the airport. Other tourists are there too, phones in their right hand, mango lassis in their left. On the wall outside the local boys sit, cross-legged, connecting into the Wi-Fi as well. This café is a hub of life.

At midnight the café closes so I join the Wi-Fi lineup on the wall. Ellowyn's flight arrives at 3am, so I keep her company through her stopover in Mumbai. And I don't call Amadou.

It's busy, at the wall, and not just with the boys. The town's dogs have woken from their day of sleep and are ranging the lanes in bristling packs. The boys carry big sticks and pull their legs up. I pull mine up as well and sit cross-legged as the dogs pant and run below in the soft Indian night.

When my taxi arrives, I slip down the wall straight into

the car. We drive through dark narrow lanes, and I worry quite a lot. At the main road we are pulled over by the police. They shine their torch on Raj, the driver. 'Just a uniform check,' he tells me. 'They make taxi drivers wear these hot uniforms and fine us if we don't.' It's sort of reassuring to see the police out in the middle of the night on these lonely roads, but also sort of not.

At the airport Raj and I have to wait outside on the street for only passengers are allowed inside the terminal. I start to panic. How will we find each other outside in this crowd and in this dark? Will she even think to walk outside? Which door will she come out of? I stand in the thick crowd under a light and wait. I worry and worry.

Raj sees her first. He points to the crowd at the bag carousel and says, 'That one must be yours.' He is right, she is mine. That one. My glorious girl, looking terribly thin and tall and all grown up.

There was no need for any of that worry. But, still, I cry with relief and she laughs and here we are. Both safe. Both having negotiated the world. Both here together on an Indian footpath at 4am on a Thursday morning.

She talks a lot in the car at first, then as the morning light mists through she spends more time looking out the window. We drive past apartment blocks, past lagoons edged with high coconut trees, past tarpaulin shacks, past people asleep in the shade of trees. She holds my hand in the back seat and sometimes her chin gives a little wobble. There is quite a lot to look at out there and it's been a long journey.

She mostly sleeps that first day, and I get to smooth her hair while she does. I'm back being a mum, having a sleeping child in front of me that I can watch over, and it feels good.

In the evening I sit out on our verandah, my feet on the cool tiles. I look across at the neighbour's giant mango tree. It's so big the whole of it doesn't fit in my vision; I have to turn my head to take it all in. The edges of it seem to glow when it gets dark and turn the night into magic.

In the morning we walk along the beach to the supermarket. Ellowyn attracts all eyes and all phones. It seems she has turned into a supermodel since I saw her last.

The beach is full of young men who all want a photo with her. They yell across the sand, 'Just one selfie! I have come a long way to see you!' At first, she finds it fun. She stands and poses with as many men as can squeeze themselves into the picture.

But it quickly becomes awful. 'Mum, Mum,' she whispers, 'where are all the women?' I can't see any either, just crowds of smiling men in tight swimming togs, pushing themselves forward, wanting to be seen, wanting eye contact, wanting an arm across a shoulder. Wanting.

We put our heads down and pick our way through the water bottles lining the sand. They roll in the surf, banging against our legs. Some men pretend to photograph the beach just as we walk by. Bolder ones run after us, 'Please, please, please!' they shout. It seems Ellowyn is the sight these tourists have come to see. They want to swim in the waves with her, to dance on the beach all night. They want to be wild and free with her.

The supermarket is worth the walk. It is brand new and full of things from all over the world. Guava juice from Vietnam, salsa from Spain, cheese from France. We choose curry rolls from India. Still hot and baked just down the road.

It has air conditioning as well. We find the coldest vents and stand under them, drying the sweat from our backs. By lucky chance the coldest vent is the one near the beauty products. Ellowyn loves these: anything in little wrapped packets. She stands there for a long, long time choosing a bar of soap and drying her back.

We take our curry rolls home and eat them on our verandah and wave to Manuel. I think he is relieved to see me happy and with company. He wanders down and introduces his dogs to Ellowyn. He has a lot of them, and their bodies are hard with muscle and rage. They strain at their chains and bark madly. Two of them roam the garden, off leash. 'These are the friendly ones,' Manuel tells us, 'Asha and Bala. Don't touch the others.'

Ellowyn loves dogs and she wants them to love her back. She tries to befriend these two off-leash ones. She crouches down, hand extended and calls their names. They bark furiously and back away.

She leaves chips in their sleeping cupboard, which is outside our front door. 'This is a sign of my deep love,' she declares and indeed it is not like her to give away chips. They eat them, quickly, suspiciously, and bark again. She sings their names, 'Asha, Bala, I love you.' They bristle, furious.

At lunchtime they are let out into the lane for a run. Asha comes back limping, holding up her back foot. Manuel runs his hands over his bald head. 'She has been stoned,' he says. 'There are some people here who hate my grandparents. They stone my dogs now for something that happened long ago.'

Ellowyn is shocked. She tries to get closer to Asha, to give her more chips to make up for the stoning, but the dog is doubly wary now. 'What can I do?' Manuel says. 'What can I do?'

Ellowyn wore a pair of white pants on the plane here. She uses the bar of soap from the supermarket to wash them out in a bucket in the garden. She hangs them over the back of a chair on the verandah to dry overnight. In the morning there are only shreds of pants left. We find some scraps of white cotton in the garden. She has underwear that is missing too, that we never find. The only explanation is the dogs, her friends the dogs. Asha and Bala have ripped apart her pants when we were sleeping.

They are there the next morning, panting, watching us, wanting chips. 'Mum, Mum, what do I do?' she says. 'Better keep feeding them chips,' I say, 'keep them as sweet as we can.'

Manuel has a lot of friends here. Men roar up the lane on their Royal Enfield motorbikes. They clang through the pink gates and sit with Manuel on his verandah. They come at all times of the day and stay until late. In the evenings there is a crowd up there. They talk and drink and wave out to us.

His friend Rahul arrives one evening, looking cool in his black leather on his black bike with his black hair slicked back. He parks just in the gates by our hut and stops at our verandah for a chat. 'I'm Goan,' he says. 'Really, I'm from Bombay, but I'm Goan. I have the heart of a Goan.'

Manuel shakes his head 'NO' in the background and looks down at the earth, scuffing shapes with his toes.

'I'm here for the nightlife, the beach parties and the drinking,' he says to me. 'What are you here for?'

I don't really have an answer for that, I can't say, 'I'm

here to sort out my daughter, fill up my emptiness, and ease my bitterness.' Those aren't things you can say publicly, not to someone you don't know and not when your own daughter is listening. So I just shrug and say, 'I'm here for a holiday, a rest.'

He turns to Ellowyn. 'I will come back and take your mother on a date and we will go to nightclubs. All the men will want her photo, but I will be the only one to have it.' His smile is wide, his shoulders held high, his chest puffed up. 'It will be me that is the lucky one for once,' he boasts.

In the morning Manuel picks up fallen coconut leaves at the back of our hut. He bundles them up, ready for the afternoon fire, and puts them in a pit made in the upturned roots of a coconut tree. He calls me over and warns me of the nightclubs, the beach parties and the drinking. 'Don't let your daughter go alone,' he tells me quietly, 'and don't you go alone. Best to not go at all, either of you.'

I tell him Ellowyn and I have other things to do here, sorting out things. He sighs and touches my arm, 'Good luck then,' he says, 'with the daughter and with the sorting. Keep her away from the nightclubs or you will have more sorting than you know what to do with.'

It is a good place for talking here and Ellowyn and I have a lot to talk about. Some of it is very hard, some we have to abandon while Ellowyn cries in the bathroom. I sit on the verandah and watch as Manuel lights the daily fire. The leaves flare up quickly, crackling. The smoke rises, hangs in the air and somehow manages to break and mend things.

The Virgin Mary watches the fire too. And the sorting. Mary's glass door streams with condensed water all day, and it seems that she cries too, in her house just outside the bathroom window. Her door has warped in its frame and there is a small gap. Just enough for her to slip in and out of. And I think she does, sometimes. I think she slips out and holds Ellowyn's hand for a bit. Maybe mine too.

On Sunday we get up early and walk down the beach to church. With Mary right outside our door it seems the polite thing to do. Besides, a bit of praying might help both of us, I think. The tide has washed away the plastic bottles from last night and we paddle in clear water all the way. Our feet become green rippling jewels.

The church rises white out of the coconut grove. Inside are dark wooden beams, painted statues and a colonial Jesus. We squash into a pew at the back, into the comfort of a church service. And it feels like we are safe here. The world has not gone mad. We are not on the brink of planetary destruction. All is well. Jesus loves the little children and it is right to live life slowly, under the coconuts.

When we get back there is a frog in our toilet, floating in the water bowl. It has a red back and legs that look very strong. Ellowyn puts a stick in the toilet so it can crawl out, but it doesn't. It just sits there.

So we walk up the lane to the café to use their toilet, and sit on the wall to use their Wi-Fi. We give the frog lots of time to leave. When we get home, it is still there, and another one has come. A grey lumpy frog clings to the mirror. Ellowyn whispers, 'We should have looked up poisonous frogs when we were on the wall.'

Now it is dark. The dogs are out. We can hear them howling and panting. Using our own bathroom is the only way.

'So,' she says, 'where do I wee? Inside on top of the frog?

Or do I go outside, maybe on top of a frog and a snake? And what about Asha and Bala? What do I do?'

I say, 'You make your own choices, then you deal with the consequences. This is what we've been trying to sort out. Choices and consequences.'

'But what do you do, Mum, when the consequences are bad either way?' she asks. I don't know the answer to this. It's so easy to give advice when I think I can see the right way, but I don't know what to do when both choices are bad. Ellowyn sits and thinks for a long time, then she goes outside.

Later she tries the shower in the bathroom. She thinks the frogs may not notice her off to the side, in the shower. But very quickly there is banging and screaming. She rushes out, 'That's a very fast frog! It's a very good jumper. A very good jumper,' she gasps, clutching a towel, wet haired, wild eyed. 'We were right to be cautious of that frog; it's very lucky I did an outside wee.'

We keep the bathroom door closed and put the towel along the door crack underneath. 'If frogs can come in then what else can?' she whispers. Rahul has been telling her stories of black pythons 11 metres long and of a snake catcher who traps them in a giant sock. He has shown her videos of it on his phone.

Rahul begins to come around more and more. To visit Manuel he says, but both men end up sitting on our verandah in the evenings. We talk about business. 'Money is the only thing given respect now,' Manuel says, 'but there is no respect in the way you make it. Drug dealers get respect and an honest man gets nowhere. If I don't have a gold watch on my wrist, I am nothing.'

I look at Manuel, an old man with a bent, tired body, and I know he is right. We all know he is right. Rahul nods his head and sighs. Mary knows it too. She has stood witness to this his whole life. She has seen it all, there in her grotto. The old arguments, the stoning of dogs, the injustice. The best she can do for now is to cry the tears that run down the glass door. 'What can I do?' Manuel says. 'What can I do?'

Rahul says, 'You can party. That's what I do when I can't bear things. I just go out and party.' It does seem the main strategy of Rahul's life, to party. Every time he comes to visit he yells from the gate, 'Ellowyn, I have come to take your mother out to party.'

It surprises me when one night I say, 'Okay then Rahul, let's see if that works, let's go and party.'

Rahul is delighted. He throws his arm over my shoulder, whips out his phone, and says, 'We must take a selfie first!'

Manuel says he will stay here with Ellowyn, and he will wait up for me. He touches my shoulder and murmurs, 'Be careful, even with Rahul, be careful.'

Even though the club is 10 minutes' walk away, Rahul insists we go on his bike. I hop on the back and put my arms around his waist. And it feels good. I almost lay my head against his shoulder, but I realise it won't work for the selfie Rahul is taking. I look up and smile instead.

There is no one in the first club. The music thumps out, announcing wild times, but inside no one is there. Just flashing lights and walls shaking with the boom. I'm happy to have the dance floor all to myself; I like lots of room for dancing, but Rahul wants to go where there are people. 'I want to see everyone,' he shouts over the music. 'Let's go somewhere else and dance and take selfies.'

The next place is packed. I think everyone just comes to the one club. Every man that is. I don't see any women at all; really, I am the only one. I send a prayer of gratitude to Manuel, thanking him for his warning about Ellowyn. She would be overwhelmed here. I stick close to Rahul's side. We sit on cane chairs overlooking the sea, while trance music spins. Rahul is exuberant. He orders Feni and insists it's poured in front of us. 'No spiking drinks for us,' he yells. His phone is out all night. We dance for the selfies, eat for the selfies, drink for the selfies, have fun for the selfies. The selfies rule.

When he takes me home, he tells me he has to go back to Mumbai for work. 'I will come down next weekend,' he says, 'and we will go to the club again.'

But I am done with the clubs and the selfies. I tell him it's time for Ellowyn and me to do some sightseeing. No more clubbing.

It's quieter during the week when the men have gone back to work. It's easier to leave our garden, easier to walk to places.

On Wednesday, there is a market down at the beach. Ellowyn is breathless with excitement; markets are her all-time favourite things. Besides, she needs to buy some new pants.

She gets up early on market day. When I wake up, she is sitting on her bed, all her money spread out in piles around her. It's a tricky conversion rate between Indian rupees and New Zealand dollars so she has put her rupees in bundles to make shopping easier.

We are the first ones at the market. We are so early the traders are still setting up their stalls. White canvas is strung up between coconut trees, rickety bamboo rails are lashed together to make little shops. We eat samosas and watch the market come alive.

In a quiet corner the Tibetans set up their stalls. They have driven down from their refuge in Dharamsala for summer trading. They all sit together, cross-legged and quiet on the ground under the white tarpaulins. Their silence seems to make their wares even more precious. They sell treasures from their tortured, splendid kingdom: woollen blankets, jewellery, prayer flags, incense burners. Beautifully crafted things. Cold mountain things.

I sit on a low stool and look at the jewellery laid out on the ground. I hold up earrings, to see how they catch the light, and we talk of our homes, the Tibetan woman and me. 'It's snowing at home right now,' she says. 'One day I might see that. One day I might see the high places of home.'

It's hard to imagine having never seen home. Or to imagine snow when it's this hot here. But I know the feeling of high cold mountains and we sit with that feeling for a while. And I understand that you need to really belong to a land, to have a home where your ancestors have stood. To have lineage, connection. I understand the search for home.

There are traders here from all over this continent. From Kashmir, Gujarat, Kathmandu, from Rajasthan, it seems from everywhere. They nod and smile. They say they are Goan now. But, secretly, inside they aren't. They all want to go home.

I am stopped by a man in the market. He touches my arm and says, 'Please, I am writing a book, can I have a minute to talk about your home? just a quick interview?' I like talking about home and I'm happy to help with a book.

We sit in one of the cafés looking out over the beach. We have a beer. He sits there, with his man bun, his white singlet, his wooden prayer beads. He sits there looking really cool. He doesn't talk at all.

I ask, 'What's your book about?'

He says, 'Do you find me attractive?'

I look out to sea, and I sigh a little inside.

'What parts of me are attractive?' he pushes.

I look back at him and say, 'Have you started your book?' There is silence. Then he asks me out for a drink, even though we are having a drink right now.

He says, 'I like yoga. Have you come here to do yoga? Will you do yoga with me?'

I stand up to leave and say, 'I hope you find what you are looking for.'

He shouts after me, 'Wait! It is you! It is you I am looking for! Can I have one selfie with you? Just one selfie!'

Just there, just a few steps down from the café, is the beach and it is bursting with men like this, and it feels like they are all looking, all wanting their one selfie. The sun blasts, music pumps and in a white haze of heat men shout. They splash and cluster around the boat rides. They jostle and wrestle each other. And all the time keep their eyes out to see who is watching them.

Mostly it's the cows that watch them. Sitting on the hard wet sand at the high-tide mark the cows spend the day hanging out down at the beach wreathed in marigold flowers. The cows are really good at staring. They don't blink much. Decorated in yellow and orange, they just watch these young men.

Back in the market I see him again, my man bun man.

He has his hand on a woman's arm and says to her, 'I am writing a book, can I interview you for my book?'

I meet Ellowyn, she points out the man and says, 'Mum, he wanted to interview me too, but turns out he's not writing a book, he just wants a selfie.'

We wander home in the dusk and find a man waiting at our front gate. He hisses, 'You have stolen my house.' He swears at us in the dark, angry and vicious. He wants to know how long we are staying, how much we are paying. He says, 'Manuel is a bastard for giving away my house.'

Ellowyn and I edge close to Mary, glowing white in the dark. 'We know nothing,' I say. 'We have to sleep.'

In the morning he stops at the café and accuses us again of thievery. He talks loudly about us to the other tourists; he throws dirty looks at us. He comes in the afternoon and takes the clay pots lining the verandah. 'These are mine,' he hisses. He pulls the plants out and they lie wilting in the shade. The plants aren't his. The earth isn't his. The house isn't his. But it seems the clay pots are.

Manuel is upset, and he doesn't understand the anger or the assertion of ownership. 'Sometimes he stays here, but he didn't book, or write, or phone. The house is mine, not his.'

It is odd to be in the middle of an argument, to be whispered about. It's strange to be hated. Me and my lovely girl. So we leave the shady lanes and start spending more time at the beach. It's good to get away from the whispers. But the beach is hot and difficult. Ellowyn is surrounded by men as soon as we get down there. The only escape is to sit in a café. The ones that have an upstairs are best, away from the gaze of the men.

There are rumours of very bad things happening on this

narrow edge of land, in these cafés. But we lean back, put our feet up on the rails and watch the sun set. The hot wind blows across the sea from Yemen, and all the built-up heat of the day intensifies in the last fiery moments of the sun. We talk of Arabia in front of us and India behind us and of life, and consequences. And I wonder how any mother can let her daughter go.

Rahul comes back on the weekend. He clangs in through the gate, waves to Manuel and stops on our verandah. 'I have come to take you sightseeing,' he declares. 'I like the nightclubs better, but let's be tourists and take selfies all weekend.'

We go off to the abandoned splendour of Old Goa with Rahul and the other tourists. Big tour buses full of Indian families pour into the old capital as well, and it is crowded. Ellowyn and I can't help but stand out here, with our straw hats to keep off the fierce sun and our upward gazes at these European churches.

This town was settled in the wrong place Rahul tells us; it was too swampy, full of bad air and malaria. The capital has now moved down river to Panaji, but the old buildings remain and pull us all.

Rahul insists on selfies, then he disappears inside the Basilica to have a look around. The signs outside say 'Keep Silence. Mass/Marriage going on'. We see neither Mass nor marriage. We hear no silence.

We hear, 'Please, just one selfie, just one selfie.' And this time it is both of us that are in hot demand for family photos. It's a lot harder to say no to grandmothers than it is to young men.

So we stand for photo after photo, squinting into the

sun. Little babies are thrust into our arms, grandmas put their arms around our waists, children press their bodies tightly against our legs. We stand against the pink wooden doors of the basilica, and smile. Jesus and Rahul inside at our backs.

Rahul comes out, waves and rushes off to the next old building, leaving Ellowyn and me backed up against the basilica doors. I murmur to Ellowyn, 'That's enough, we must move on, see the sights,' but a grandma approaches with a smile and a phone and grandchildren.

Ellowyn asks, 'What can we do, Mum? What can we do?'

All we see of Old Goa are those old doors. Rahul comes back an hour later, and we are still there, with a long line of families in front of us. He pushes up, takes my arm and steers me to a taxi. 'You should say no,' he says. 'It's crazy, people are obsessed with selfies around here.'

That evening there is a concert in our local café. We can hear the bass from our verandah and as we walk down for dinner the music becomes really loud. Posters plaster the trees down the lane, advertising the band's world tour.

The café is empty when we arrive, but the boy band is in full performance. They don't seem to have noticed they have no audience.

The boys jump around on the stage. They have sunglasses on and caps on backwards. They film each other and shout into the camera, 'This party is going off in Goa tonight!' They close their eyes, screw up their faces, toss their hair, raise their knees to their chests on the high notes.

'The world is watching!' one screams out.

Ellowyn stands up and goes to the shop next door.

Rahul only has eyes for his phone. But I'm there, representing the world. I can't stay long though; it's exhausting being the only audience member in the world. Besides, Rahul says we have to get up early in the morning, for he is taking us bird watching.

We do get up very early, and it's so dark it seems it will never be day again. Fog hovers over the rice fields, layering the world with white intensity. We catch the commuters ferry over the river and stand silent while the ferry churns in the current. We all watch the sun rise, an orange ball through the white fog.

Our canoe arrives, and with it The Birdman of Goa. He squats behind us in the canoe, up on the edge. He taps Ellowyn on the shoulder, 'Look! look! A kingfisher, an egret, a brahminy kite, a heron.' His quick, bird-trained eyes spot things we didn't even know live here.

He steers us up little inlets to look for birds in the muddy banks. Mangroves crowd above us, filtering the light. Crocodile tracks slither down the mud, 'Very recent,' he whispers, paddling us closer to the bank, 'very fresh tracks.' Ellowyn, Rahul and I shuffle a little close to the middle of the canoe. The Birdman, though, hangs a little further out over the edge.

There are fishermen out on the water too, their own canoes in small lines on the quiet estuary. And all this could be a thousand years ago. We drift around the swampy lagoons, our eyes sharpening up to what is here.

The brahminy kite, the heron, the kingfisher, the egret.

We repeat them back, arms pointing, a liturgy, an incantation of the magic of this world, and I am grateful we can see some of these immense treasures.

Rahul has spent his whole weekend with us. 'I love being a tourist!' he says. He has to go back to Bombay for work on Monday, but he promises he will be back and be a tourist with us again. And it feels nice to know he will come back. I realise I'm getting very fond of Rahul, and I'm relying on him to make me laugh.

I don't even mind the selfies now; indeed I think I look really good in some of them. Sometimes I find myself saying, 'Quick Rahul, a selfie!'

At breakfast the next day there is a man at the next table with his leg up on a seat. His leg has gone purple and the white bandages around his calf are seeping with blood. It drips into the dust. 'Last night,' he is shouting to all the tourists eating breakfast, 'last night I was sitting on the wall using the cafe's Wi-Fi and this bloody great dog attacked me.'

His leg looks bad; it's mottled, swollen. He has spent the night at the doctor's, having rabies shots and being sewn up. He is really shaken and so are we. 'These dogs look dead during the day, and at night they become lunatics,' he shouts angrily.

I turn to Ellowyn, 'I think we have to wee on the frog from now on,' I whisper. 'No more going outside after dark. Our very own dogs would do this to us.'

'I know, Mum,' she says, 'look what they did to my pants.'

Our last week is spent visiting the local towns. Ellowyn has researched them using the café's Wi-Fi and she works out when the markets are. We spend days edging through rows of chillies, bananas, fish, keeping to the shady overhangs.

The best part, though, are the flower markets, deep

inside old buildings. Blossoms are piled into soft heaps, all ready for stringing into garlands for shop fronts, temples, buses. Huge cane baskets are full of marigolds, asters, jasmine and roses. It is all shadows and glowing flowers. No one talks to us; they know we are not here to buy. We are only here to look at the piles and piles of beauty. We walk slowly, we take big breaths of flowers.

On the other side of a flower market, near a bus station, we find Krishnamoorti, a perfumist. He sits up high in a glass booth, shining out in yellow and orange robes. He has flashing rings, a gold hat, and a large presence. He lounges on an office swivel chair, and a cheetah skin thrown over the high back turns it into a throne. For 1000 rupees he will read your soul and mix your matching perfume.

He has a lot of customers. A busload of Russian women has arrived and they all want their souls read, some more than once. Women push onto the wooden seats, waiting in big clumps. Ellowyn and I join in the queue, but we don't ever get near the front. Women pretend to talk with their friend further up the line, then they are back for a second soul reading.

Krishnamoorti beckons to me. He tells me he is tired, 'It is too hard to read all these Russian souls, even though I am trying my best,' he says. 'I need another nationality of soul.'

He tells me to tell them no more. 'Who is the last?' he asks. I point to a woman wearing a white shirt that says 'YES' in glitter. 'Then that one is the last. Our "Yes" lady is the last. Then I will read you and your daughter's souls.'

I tell the Russians, but they don't seem to understand, even when the Indian women watching translate. More come. They push up to the counter, they video everything, they want selfies, they want their souls read again and again.

Ellowyn sits down on the concrete guttering, head in her hands. She feels sick, it's too hot and dirty and suddenly everything is too overwhelming. I see her shoulders shake a bit and I know it's time to leave. Even without the reading of our souls.

Krishnamoorti has an assistant, small and innocuous, barely noticeable. He comes out of the glass booth and stands in front of the women. He insists they leave. He barricades Krishnamoorti behind the glass window, his arms stretched wide. 'No more! No more!' he shouts. 'You must leave now! Now!'

I help Ellowyn up and we turn to leave, but the assistant is at my elbow, steering us to the window. I sit on the high stool at the counter and say, 'I'm sorry, we are all too tired, let us all go home and rest.'

Krishnamoorti takes a long slow look at me. He looks so deeply, so intensely that I stop talking. He breathes, a big slow inhale, then a long exhale. He gives a large slow smile. He says loudly, 'Oh, you are wonderful! Oh! Oh!' He puts a hand on his heart. 'Oh my, such wonder!'

Ellowyn hears and bursts out laughing. His head swivels to her, and he beckons her over to the other seat. He looks at both of us and breathes slowly and smiles, and it feels like we all know each other, and always have, and suddenly we are all smiling and tears are running down our faces.

He looks into Ellowyn's eyes. 'This one is perfect! This one is marvellous!' he exclaims. 'This one is full of light!'

Inhaling deeply, he swings his throne to the side. He raises one arm, his rings flash gold in the mirror behind him.

With a flourish he shouts, 'I need Rose!' His attendant pulls a bottle off the shelf, hovers to the side and with a bow presents the bottle of rose essence. 'And I need Lotus Flower! To hold her heart!'

His eyes glisten with tears, he smiles, he shakes the potion. He calls for more: geranium, jasmine, jonquil. He breathes deeply. He asks for my wrist and draws a circle and a line with the perfume. I smell it.

I am startled. He has put my soul into that smell, I know this is me. It smells of quiet, intimate pleasure. He leans close in and whispers, 'I know you know how to use this. Be sure to use it like it should be used.'

He turns to Ellowyn, breathes deeply, smiles. Tears are in his eyes. He holds the moment for a long time, then he shouts, 'I need Pure Jasmine!' Pure Jasmine! It must be Absolutely Pure!'

His assistant reaches for a tiny bottle on the top shelf, one full of gold. Krishnamoorti leans closer and whispers to Ellowyn that she is blessed. And it suddenly feels like he is telling her secret truths from the other side. He says that she is golden and perfect and although bad times may come to always remember what she is. We leave in a daze of golden loveliness, crying and laughing, and nothing can take the magic from us. Not the dead chickens, or the heat, or the dogs. We slid into heaven in Krishnamoorti's shop and we have some of it now in a little glass bottle.

I think we have just found a cure for depression. Krishnamoorti himself. Half an hour with Krishnamoorti looking into your eyes, telling you that you are marvellous and sending you away with flower perfume that is a reading of your soul changes everything. He has done more good for

Ellowyn than all my mother talks on the verandah have. I realise I should have brought her straight here from the airport and kept my own mouth shut.

We catch a tuk-tuk home, clutching our soul's essence on the bumpy drive. We slide the windows open and peer out. Houses quickly fall back into the jungle here. Vines grow overnight. Seeds find footholds on window sills and the next day a tree is there. Life pushes up as we rattle down tiny tracks, short cuts and back lanes through the tall coconuts.

At home the frog has still not left the toilet. Ellowyn watches it carefully and announces that the toilet bowl is actually its home pond. When we think it has gone it has just crawled up under the rim. She tells me it swims against the flush, 'It's strong and determined, that frog.' She talks to it a lot. I hear her when she goes in there. She says, 'Dude, it's just not healthy in there, you've got to find a healthier place to live.'

I lie on the bed, exhausted. I say, 'I'm so tired Ellowyn, I'm too tired to even make it to the toilet.'

She replies, 'Mum, I will turn on the light for you, I will check the room for snakes for you, but I will not wee on the frog for you.'

Manuel says we should stay, 'You fit in here,' he says, 'lots of people just stay. They become Indian, or that's what we all think. But I really don't know, I don't know what they become, and I don't think they do either.'

I can see how easy that would be. To stay and become something else and to not know what that is. To fill the empty spaces inside with life here and to end up not knowing what or who I have become.

We have met other tourists here, many who know this place, who keep coming back. Every summer for years they come back, for a month, for five. They come to sit all morning under pink bougainvillea and watch white butterflies. Or to watch a pile of leaves burn. Or to lie in an afternoon's heat haze under a slow fan. They walk the shady dusty paths, for these are potent, powerful things to do.

We walk under coconut palms in the golden green light and talk about dinner. We sit on the balcony in the evening with Manuel and watch the glowing mango tree. It would be easy to lose myself here, to block out all the stuff I don't want to feel. To stay for 20 years and emerge bewildered and bleary-eyed into the world again and think I had only been gone a week.

It's hard to say goodbye. Rahul tells me to come back next year, that he will have the latest phone by then. He says, 'Next year you will come back happier, ready to party with me. I will wait for you.' We take lots of selfies on the verandah. Then he roars off on his bike.

It's even harder to say goodbye to Manuel. He gives me a hug and whispers in my ear, 'You have done well, to sort the daughter, and sort yourself.'

Ellowyn shakes out a whole packet of chips in the cupboard for the dogs. She keeps her bottle of soul perfume in her pocket. 'I need it, to make the trip home,' she says, 'it helps to know that Krishamoorti believes in me.'

Our plane to Mumbai is filled with men. I think all the men from the beach are with us today. I look to the back and men's eyes meet mine, bold and wanting to be seen. They are full of the delight, the supreme specialness of being a man. They take selfies of themselves sitting in their plane seats.

The male energy is so big, so intense it seems to give the plane an extra boost. We lift off in a massive rattle, a shuddering surge of energy so big it releases the oxygen masks.

In Mumbai we part. I see Ellowyn to her gate, back to New Zealand and her studies. I have a flight to Turkey. I haven't finished with the Mediterranean yet; it has called me back. It's hard to let her go, but I figure that's what this is all about, this life thing. Making your own choices. Dealing with the consequences. Letting go.

# SEVEN

# The Delight

TURKEY

I WAKE WAY TOO EARLY, THE SUN IN MY EYES. IT'S A bright sun, a different quality of sun. I lie and look at the river reflecting in wobbles on my ceiling. It feels like I am on a houseboat, here in this campground. There is splashing outside my window. Oars I think, or birds.

I arrived late, to a town already asleep. I have woken up early and still the town sleeps. It's nice, though, to walk down the river path in the morning all alone. The mountains rise high to my right and are still flicked with snow. The river splashes with fish.

And it feels like I've landed back in my childhood. It feels like I know this place already.

All morning I drink coffee, sitting on the banks of the river. Slowly other tourists come out of their hotels and drink coffee too. Then I start to eat: kebabs, grilled peppers, pomegranate tarts. I eat so much that when I stand to leave the chef runs out and shakes my hand. I tell him he has the best food in all of Turkey and I'm pretty sure this is true.

I stay up late, even though I'm jet-lagged. I sit on the river bank and watch the stars come out. The burial tombs on the far bank are lit up. The moon reflects itself in the water, frogs croak quietly and then I hear 'Beautiful lady, would you like to come on my boat and look at the stars from here?'

That is exactly what I want to do. And it doesn't sound corny at all, not here. It just sounds genuine. Because who wouldn't want to look at stars from a boat? I step over the wooden side and wobble out to the front, where there is a carpet laid down. I sit down, lean back on the thick cushions and look up at the sky.

We lie there, in the silence, just looking at the stars, while the boat moves quietly in the rushes. I am startled at how nice it is to be in silence with a stranger; to say nothing, to expect nothing. I'm not sure if the man beside me falls asleep or not, he is so quiet. But when I feel sleep start to settle on me I quietly leave, rocking the boat as I go.

In the morning I go back down the path, back to my coffee shop and there is my boat from last night. The motor is going, it is full of tourists. The captain is there, in his captain's hat, the man from last night waving. He shouts, 'Quick! quick! I have been waiting for you!'

He throws me an orange, then he throws open his arms. He shouts, 'My boat is your boat! Come with us!' So I do. I clamber over the side to the front, where we watched the stars from last night. The carpet and the cushions are still there. I lean back and eat my orange and it's as if I never left.

We putt slowly up the river, the boat pushing through tall river grass. Then the engine is cut and we just drift. The captain clambers to the front where I am and leans out over the rail to part the rushes. He takes my hand and pulls me up to show me a bird's nest, hidden deep in the rushes. Our eyes meet over the four speckled eggs. 'My name is Kostas,' he murmurs, giving my hand a squeeze, 'and I am very pleased you came back.'

The mother bird flaps and cries out. Kostas pushes the boat away. 'I am taking all these tourists to market,' he says, pointing up the river to the town at the head of the lake. The tourists on board gaze out to the town too, their hands clutching their shopping bags, wanting those early-morning bargains. Kostas whispers to me, 'It's best to go late, that's when you get the bargains. We should be spending all morning swimming.'

There are many boats just like ours, skimming up the lake like a flock of birds. 'Can't we go faster?' a woman asks Kostas, 'That boat will beat us.' She points to a boat off to our left. 'Maybe they didn't stop to look at bird nests,' she says with a nasty look at me.

There is plenty in the market, even for late comers like us. I stop at a stall and buy some Turkish delight. The stall holder has six eggs for sale too, a big jar of pickles, some woven yurt rope and a lumpy block of olive soap.

I admire her stall, and her fashion. She has on loose flowery pants, a woollen vest, a flowered head scarf. Then, looking down, I see pretty much that's exactly what I have on. Put me in a head scarf and I'm there. Indistinguishable.

It feels like these women know it too. They wave out to me, put their hand on my back in a hug, and pull me in from the stream of people. They talk to me in Turkish and look puzzled when I reply in English.

And all the while layers of canvas gently lift and drop

overhead. They overlap, tied under and over each other and move with the wind.

I saunter back to the boat with my delight and Kostas is there too. He has bought watermelon. I add the sweets to the plate of cut watermelon and we sit out the front, on the carpet, to eat together.

We sit close, our arms brushing one another. I tell him about home and show him pictures of Billy and Ellowyn. He shows me photos of his adult daughter, his grandson, and tells me he has always wanted to see kangaroos.

And so we laugh together, and I feel quite drunk even though I haven't drunk anything. I notice he eats all the white off his watermelon, going right down to the green rind. I think of Antonio, I smile, and I eat all the white off mine too.

There is no rush on the way home. The others unwrap their shopping and we all admire their bargains. Then we stop for an afternoon swim in the lake. All of us get in, even the ones who can't swim. They bob around with water floats, close to the boat, holding onto the ladder. Kostas dives in again and again, checking on us all. I swim over to the small channels in the rushes, looking for more bird nests, looking for quiet, secret things.

After a long swim, Kostas calls us all back on board. He sits in his captain's chair, leaning back into the sun, and the boat slowly putters back down the lake. I sit with my feet dangling over the edge, making my own waves with my toes.

Kostas starts humming to himself. Everyone looks quickly away, out to the lake, embarrassed. But Kostas doesn't notice or care. He sings a little louder, puts his hands up in the air and does a little dance in his seat. He swings

around and around in his captain's chair. The tourists talk
loudly and pretend they can't hear or see.

Suddenly I am sick of it. Sick of being an uptight tourist,
sick of looking away, of not joining in. So I turn round,
stand up, put my arms in the air and match his dance.

Kostas leans over and cuts the engine. He stands up,
twirls me around, claps his hands, sings louder. I clap and
spin and it feels like I really am very drunk.

Kostas turns the sound system on. Abba bursts out over
the lake, 'Loving you loving me, aha.' And boom. Everyone
leaps up and starts dancing, on this riverboat, in the middle
of this lake, in the middle of this day. There are people
clapping and yelling, people spinning and laughing, and it
goes on and on. We are all intoxicated with the dance, the
lake, the air, the bargains.

And life is a very intoxicating thing when there are
four eggs in a bird's nest, watermelon rind, and a
handsome captain to dance with. Kostas does look more
handsome by the minute. His hair has curled with the lake
water, and in his swimming gear he looks strong and
adventurous.

Besides, the most attractive man is one that dances and
sings. He throws an arm over my shoulder and spins me to
face him. Into my ear he whispers, 'You are here, and I am
here, so why not be here together?'

Why not indeed.

Later, when the tourists have gone, we take the boat
back up the river. Kostas cooks me dinner on the BBQ
jutting out over the back of the boat. The smoke from the
coals rises into the pine trees and the white rocks. I swim
while he cooks. I watch the sunlight dapple my arms and I

think of that poem, 'Glory be to God for dappled things'. Bubbles of joy rise inside me, up into the dappled light.

An inch under this blue sea, almost not living in the sea at all, but in the air, are thousands of tiny fish. They are see-through sprats of the palest blue. I swim underneath them and rejoice in this swimming with sprats. I have swum with dolphins and sea turtles but right now, swimming with sprats is the best of all.

My life becomes very watery. Kostas seems to live on his boat, only going off it to get food. We take the boat up the river for night swims, we watch the stars, look for birds, we live outside. I live for weeks like this, falling in love every day with this man and this water. I know I'm living in a fantasy bubble, but I don't care.

I deflect his questions: 'Have you seen London? I would like to see London. Will you take me to see kangaroos? Shall we go and visit your mother? And what about those kids of yours?'

I don't want to think of anything but being here. I don't want to make plans or to think of the future. All I want to do is live the fairy tale with my Captain Charming.

I ask Kostas, 'How is it to be Greek in Turkey?'

He replies, 'The people are wonderful, the land is wonderful and the politics are terrible.' I ask for Greek music on the boat, but he goes red and shakes his head. Then, 'Later,' he says, 'in the dark, quietly, with just the stars. Later.' But there isn't a later, and I don't push.

We dance on the boat a lot. Dancing is the thing to do around here. There is something about the air that makes everyone want to, even the non-dancers. Out on the lake we often pass other boats where all the holidaymakers are dancing. We wave, call out to each other and laugh.

There are nervous dancers, though, ones that want to but have no moves and no confidence. I meet Ada dancing on the river bank, showing her friends some moves. The next day more people are there, and by the end of the week she's got a dance class happening every morning.

Ada tells me dancing is her new hobby. She is at least 70 but tells me she is young at heart and wants to attract adventure. 'A nice sea captain, like yours my dear, is what I'm after,' she says with a wink. Her hair is piled up so it falls everywhere, her blouse isn't buttoned very well, her skirt is tight, her heels high. 'It's all about being dishevelled darling, that's what the boys like,' she whispers. She arranges her students in lines behind her, and counts out loud, 'Seven, eight and roll and lift.'

Kostas and I sit on the boat, legs dangling over the side, and watch her class. She pulls quite an audience for this is a strange thing to be doing in this public space. Kostas sucks in his breath, ducks his head and nudges me. 'I think our Ada has forgotten to put her underwear on,' he says. 'Go and help her, this is not right for an old lady, for any lady.' Shocked, I look. He is right. Ada has forgotten.

'Seven, eight and roll and lift,' she calls.

More people gather to watch. The men stop, sit down, flick looks at each other, then back at Ada. I jump off the boat, join the class and call Ada over for help. I whisper in her ear. She smiles brightly at me, 'Yes darling, that's right, it's the devil in me. I do whatever I want here.'

I tell Kostas about the devil. He just shakes his head and mutters about mad tourists and bad behaviour. Very bad behaviour. And from an elder too. He sighs, pushes the boat off from the edge and we head downriver, to moor somewhere else.

Kostas wants to show me around. He loves his country and he wants me to love it too. So we catch the public bus up into the mountains for the day. It feels strange to sit on a bus, not a boat, and I do feel quite wobbly. Out of the window the mountains rise, much higher than my eye expects. They are covered with pine trees and white rocks. Sometimes I see women among the trees, gathering wood, their headscarves a triangle of colour down their backs. But mostly I see no one up there, in the hot white hills.

At Saklikent Gorge we get out to explore. We climb deep into the slit of the gorge, through white marble and silence. Kostas breathes, 'This, this is the most wonderful,' every few minutes, and he is right. There are blue butterflies and white cliffs and it's so beautiful it's ridiculous. Or enchanted.

It feels like there is something funny happening with time up here too. Something that says this is ancient and you too must also become ancient. We spend all day breathing slowly, turtle-like in these mountains.

We have lunch in a café sited in the middle of the river. The tables and chairs sit in the shallows, so we sit with our feet in the cold water. It is startlingly cold. Home cold. 'This is what New Zealand water is like, where I'm from in the south,' I say, pulling my feet out and tucking them under me.

Kostas laughs and says, 'No, no, only mountain water is like this, it can't be that cold in your land.'

I think of my thick wetsuit in the cupboard at home. It is

for mountain water, sea water, lake water, everything water. It is that cold at home.

But here it's only the mountain water that is cold. Out on the lake and the ocean the water is like warm jelly and there is nothing nicer than to spend the whole day in it. And that's what I do. It feels like a tonic, a health spa. I know this is working on my stress. My eye hasn't twitched since I arrived, my heart only races when I look at Kostas.

I feel well. Physically well, but underneath I know there are some things that haven't moved at all. I know that I don't want to carry the bitterness I left with, the grudges and the shame. But nothing seems to be moving those things. If I stayed here I could hide from them, pretend they aren't even a thing, but then at the end of it, there they will be. I know it.

On my birthday we catch the bus into town. Town is in the middle of its summer flowering and we walk in pink. Bright pink bougainvillea climbs up houses, and the street trees are pink oleander. Faded pink carpets hang over balconies. I think the colour of Turkey is pink. The flag insists boldly on red, yet the land insists on pink. It grows pink flowers, and it glows pink every morning and every evening.

We hang over the canal railing, look down, and there is a sea turtle gently flapping in the current. I think maybe all is not lost. Not when there are sea turtles, pink flowers and glowing mountains. And a captain with his arm around my shoulder.

Our walk to dinner takes us past the police station, bang in the middle of town. It is surrounded by barbed wire, rolled along the top wall. The sign says 'Photography

Forbidden', and there is a picture of a soldier holding a machine gun. It's all very scary.

Except underneath the barbed wire, climbing up the white plaster walls, is pink bougainvillea. The soldier on guard shuffles his broom among the fallen flowers, and I know his mind is on the backgammon game happening at the table outside.

Kostas's mind is there too. It seems backgammon is the national game here. Tables are always set up, and some coffee houses have tournaments that go all day every day. At night, I can hear the soft click of backgammon pieces as people gather outside to play.

It's a nice sound, the click of a backgammon, as opposed to the clicking of a phone. I would like to play, and I would like to get rid of my phone. But it's also my lifeline to my kids, to my home, and to my life. I don't think I'm ready yet, to let all that go.

We go to the fish market for dinner. Kostas has told me to dress up and I'm pleased I did, for this place is a lot flasher than it sounds. There are trees draped with fairy lights, white-clothed tables, and waiters. We choose our fish, then choose the restaurant to cook it. We stay a long time because good food and good company takes a long time.

I think about not going home, about just living here, about what that would be like. To swim with sprats and sea turtles, and go out to dinner and live like this always. Lots of others do it. This place is full of foreign women with Turkish men. I wonder what it would be like, once the initial wonder wears off. I wonder what winter would be like, when the tourists go and the towns shut down. What happens then?

Conversation turns to kangaroos. He really wants to see kangaroos, and London. He says, 'My friends have seen London, their girlfriends take them, but it's kangaroos I mostly want to see.'

I finally say, 'You know, there are no kangaroos in New Zealand.'

He looks startled, then says, 'Well, what do you have in New Zealand?'

I reply, 'Birds, we have birds.'

He reaches across the table and squeezes my hand, 'Well, that's perfect then. I've always wanted to see birds.'

I think maybe Kostas just wants to travel the world and I can't blame him. It's what I am doing. But here am I, thinking about staying, while Kostas is thinking about leaving.

He says he wants to come with me to New Zealand. 'I could make New Zealand my home if I wanted. Home is a technique. Once you know the ways your ancestors felt into the land, you can do it too. Anywhere. Finding home is all about technique.'

But I don't really know if he wants to find a new home. 'It wouldn't be like here,' I tell him. 'It wouldn't be living on a boat in the warm. It would be a job in a cold town.' If I was him, I wouldn't want to swap life on a warm boat. Even if he got me as well. Even if he has all the homing techniques in the world.

On the walk back to the bus we come across some tourists down at the waterfront. They are belly dancing to entertain other tourists. They have veils, full skirts, bare bellies, black eyeliner. I stop, startled. They look nothing like the Turkish belly dancers I've seen, and dance nothing like them either. Kostas murmurs, 'Tell me truthfully, are these tourists making fun of us? Is this for laughing?'

Trying to hold in my own laughter, I reply, 'No, this is the best they can do. They are trying very hard.'

Kostas turns to his neighbour, 'It is their best!' he exclaims, 'it is their best!' He claps very loudly. He cheers for them.

Maybe it's my birthday dinner that's done it, his wanting to love my home no matter what, or his reaction to the dancing, but the thought of going home with Kostas is suddenly very appealing.

But I need to think about that, on my own. I need to change things up a bit, to go up the coast by myself to have a think about things. I check out of my hut, take my last boat ride up the lake, I say goodbye to Kostas and the men at my kebab shop, and I'm back on the bus.

Surprisingly, it feels good to be riding away.

I go to Kas. A beautiful tourist town along the coast. It's filled with charming men looking for quick sales and looking for girlfriends. It's good for me to see this, the formula, the game. I start to wonder if this is Kostas as well. I'm wary. I tell everyone I'm a divorcee and I'm too sad for anything. They feel sorry for me and turn the conversation quickly to children. I show them pictures of my kids.

Everyone gasps at Ellowyn's beauty. They don't know her, but they want their son to marry her. No one wants their daughter to marry Billy. They don't even want to look at his photo, but they pore over Ellowyn's. 'Is she a good cook?' they ask. 'Is she quiet? Does she wear makeup? We don't want anyone who wears makeup.'

I think of all these qualities, none of which El has. But I

think of her warmth, her laugh, her quirkiness. I ask, 'Is he kind, your boy? Is he funny?'

They reply, 'He's going to be a doctor.' Their eyes fill with tears. They love their boys. Their doctors. I don't think it would work, Ellowyn and their boy.

My room here is a sleepout in Mehmet's backyard up the hill from a pebble beach. It's hard work at this beach, the pebbles are so big they are really rocks, and unwalkable. There is no choice but to hire a beach lounger and sun umbrella. I don't like sitting under an umbrella that is advertising things. But the water at Big Pebble is purple and silky, so it's worth it. I think of night swimming, of phosphorescence, and realise this is exactly the place I'm likely to find it.

At night I walk back down the hill to swim. I send thanks to Antonio and Carmen for showing me the joys of naked swimming and slip off my clothes in the dark. I splash out, hoping if I turn up the phosphorescence will turn up too. I swim for a long time, late into the dark night. I scan the water around me for vivid swishes of blue. I see gleams from the white pebbles on the beach, but that's all.

On the way home I stop at the mulberry tree outside the mosque, sit for a while and eat the deep black berries. Teenage boys zoom by on their motorbikes, going fast through the rose-lined streets and then it is all quiet. The street lights stop after the mosque, and I have to trust my intuition to get me home. There is a long stretch of no houses and no lights before I get to the top of the cliff and it's very, very dark.

The next day Mehmet comes out with a big stick. 'Don't go walking at night without this stick,' he says, making hitting, swishing motions with it. 'This is for the wild pigs; they will run at you in the dark. You practise before you go out tonight.' So I swish my stick in the air, pretending to hit pigs until he is satisfied that I can do it.

That night there is still no phosphorescence. But there is a lovely moon and I float in the moon path it makes on the water. I look up to the old Hellenistic temple on the cliff and wonder how many women have done this before me.

Every night for a week I go swimming for phosphorescence. But it quickly becomes swimming to have a chat with the Goddess, out there in the dark. 'What should I do?' I ask. 'What should I do?'

I go shopping. It's the best way I have found to distract my heart. I go to the second-hand book shop first, where the owner sells me a book about a second-hand book shop owner. She clutches it to her chest. 'This is the story of my people,' she says. I used to work in a second-hand book shop too. I wonder if that makes me one of her people. I don't ask, though. I just buy the book and smile.

I come across some old women selling crochet flower necklaces. They are sitting under a huge old fig tree, still crocheting. They tell me they spend the winter crocheting by their fire and the summer crocheting under this fig tree. They sit me down, show me how to do some stitches and I come away draped in crochet flowers.

The book and the flowers are good things, but what I really want is a carpet. Like the one on the front of Kostas's boat. I hover near the entrance of a carpet shop, a bit nervous. I have heard stories of people's life savings disappearing in carpet shops just like this one. I remind myself I have no life's savings so not to worry.

I am expertly welcomed, sat down, given apple tea and Akkan is the most charming of all the charming. He gestures around his shop. 'Look,' he says, 'there is no one here, no one to talk to so let's just enjoy each other's company.' He smiles. 'And let's look at beautiful things. I know you have no money, but I just love looking at beautiful things, and I know you do too.'

I stay all afternoon drinking apple tea with Akkan, while the sun blazes white hot outside. We laugh, we talk of ancestors, of craft, and modern life. We talk of tourists and travelling, how few tourists come into his shop, how they are mostly interested in the cheap copy things. And why that could be. 'Many have no life left in them,' he says, 'it all leaked out on their drive to work and back. They have saved up all their anger and let their curiosity go.'

I say, 'Maybe they are too scared to come into your shop, scared of spending too much money.' We laugh, drink more tea, and calculate underneath how much each person is willing to shift on the price of the exquisite red-rose carpet in front of me.

I walk out with my rose carpet. When I get home I lay it next to my bed and spend a long time lying there, admiring it. I lie down on it and pretend I'm back on the boat, looking at the stars with Kostas.

When I wake in the morning, I think of the river, the lake. The way it rocks the boat and the light. The way the sun shines through the pines. I think of Kostas. I think of all my childhood time spent at Lake Tarawera back in New Zealand. Now here is another magic lake, here it is again, as an adult. A double gift in a life.

I get a text, 'I miss you.' Then, 'My mother is sick.' Later, 'I have to take her to the hospital, I need you.'

I go out on a boat trip alone. I think it's good for me to be a normal tourist. The boat is filled with exhausted tourists here to rejuvenate. They pull themselves up the stairs and lie down on the mattress on the top deck in a daze.

We sail around the coast and I see Odysseus' head outlined in rocky headlands. I think of his epic journeys on these seas and have a little laugh.

I used to think those sea journeys of Greek myth were hard, rigorous, challenging, but not now. Being on the sea is the best place to be. It would be easy, in this gorgeous sea, to set off in a little boat on a 10-year voyage. There are islands everywhere, there are fish in the sea, and a gentle breeze. This sea is buoyant and friendly. There are no waves, no sharks, no big currents, no rips. This is not the wild Southern Ocean of home.

I think it would be much, much easier to be sailing your adventure like Odysseus, than to be his wife, at home lamenting and worrying, trying to keep the household together on hot dry earth, with suitors banging at the door. Odysseus had the easy bit.

He came home, though. Always, he was headed home. He was headed home even before he started.

We sail around the islands, stopping for lunch and for swims. I dive into deep purple water. I swim with sprats and have a slow drift with a sea turtle. When I get out, I lie face down on the wooden deck and shiver a little. The boat shifts, the sails lift and there is something else. There are flutes, high and melodic, playing through the mast. I lie there listening. I wonder if this is the song of the siren. If mermaids really are real. If the old gods are calling to me to stay.

A quiet settles over the boat on the way home. Most are lying down asleep or in a daze of loveliness. Little Katie sits next to me; she is here with her grandparents who are asleep on the mattresses at our feet. She is only four and is interested in picking the paint off the boat rails.

We head out to sea for a long, long time. I wonder if the captain is asleep along with all his passengers. Then, rushing up the stairs to the wheel, he yells, 'Hang on!' and turns the boat sharply to the left. But most are still sleeping or dazed and have nothing to hang on to anyway. As the boat swings around I swing Katie onto my lap and hold her tight. Nearly, very nearly she was off, flying over those rails.

Her grandparents roll across the deck and can't stand up, rubbish goes flying and bags fall off benches. But after a bit we laugh. For this is the land of sunshine and delight, and we are all safe. Katie goes back to paint picking and tells me of her magic superpowers. I stare into the distance and think of my own kids.

Billy has told me it's so cold they have bubble wrapped their flat and Ellowyn says she can't get out of bed. I reminded them to wear thermal underwear, to tuck in their tops to their underpants. I miss them. I miss home too, and those cold winters, crunching the frost up. I don't know if I can live without the cold, or without home.

That night, in a sudden despair that I haven't taught my kids enough, I send them a message, 'Do you know enough to be okay? Dental floss? Washing? Turning off switches? Hanging on to the boat rail? Everyone know stuff?'

Billy replies, 'I know none of that, and the thought of doing any of it disgusts me.'

Ellowyn doesn't answer at all.

I get more texts, 'I miss you. The boat needs repairs. I miss you.'

The next day at lunch I meet Andy and Shannon. I overhear them ordering, and I hear their Kiwi accents. They are the first Kiwis I have heard in months. We have lunch together and I tell them about Kostas. Shannon starts to laugh, 'Everyone falls in love with Turkish boat captains. Everyone. There are even films about that. Lots of films,' she laughs again.

I know she is right. I have watched some of them myself. It doesn't make it any easier, though. I say, 'I know I'm living a cliché. I know everyone's in love with the Turkish people.'

Andy shakes his head, 'Not me, not any of the blokes. We don't get to talk to the girls here. We don't even get to see them.'

It's really good to be talking to some Kiwis, and we talk about home, about our new prime minister and her baby, about their orchard. Their language is full of Kiwi slang, and I realise how much I have missed it. I also realise how right they are, about the boat captain thing. But, still.

They tell me they are here walking the Lycian Way. They have just walked the Camino and it has changed them so profoundly they say they are making their whole lives into a pilgrimage. 'All we want to do now is to walk,' Shannon says. 'The Camino took away my bitterness and my shame. I want to keep walking forever now, I feel so good.'

I can't believe I am hearing this. First, a woman who admits to having those burdens and, second, a cure. My heart beats hard, my face goes red. I push Shannon for more, for exactly what she did, exactly what happened, but she says she can't explain. 'Something just happens when you walk as a pilgrim. The Camino just does things to your insides.'

That night Kostas texts, 'Are you sure there are no kangaroos? I really want to see kangaroos.' I laugh back, but I think that what we both want are different things.

Kostas finds some New Zealand bird song on the internet and sends me the link. 'This is what I want to hear most of all,' he texts. The bird song breaks my heart. There is a tui, a bellbird, birds I know so well, birds of my garden. I cry for a bit, in my room, listening to the birds of my home. But I don't cry for Kostas. And I begin my research on the Camino.

The days get hotter, the air conditioning breaks, but it's still cooler in than out. I notice the locals pack the waterfront at night, and during the day they stay inside. I do that too. I spend the hot afternoons reading on the sofa with the windows wide open. High mountains rise to the north and the sea glitters to the west.

I read of magic and sea journeys and mountain passes, and heroic book shop owners. Glancing out my windows I see such journeys do exist. That Shannon and Andy are out there right now walking one.

Every day seems to be hotter than the last. Tensions are rising, I can feel it. Kostas texts, 'When are you coming back? I don't like you out there alone.'

At dinner I sit at a table outside under a fig tree and watch young boys kick their ball up against a wall. Suddenly there are young men too. They don't kick the ball; they kick each other. One is thrown to the ground, kicked in the ribs, the groin, the stomach.

There is yelling, grunting. The backgammon game next to me stops, and the two old men rush out. They hold the young ones in arm locks. They wait for tempers to calm. But it's so hot and these boys want to kick.

People are on edge; there is an election in two weeks. Kostas texts, 'Do you understand me? I don't want you out there alone.'

My leaving date is coming up. I go back to Kostas to say goodbye. The magic is still there, but I also see the reality. If I stayed I would be living a fantasy, a pretence. I still have things to sort out inside me. And Kostas doesn't want to stay anyway. We laugh, and cry a little, we try not to argue, and try to leave the best we can.

So much of my time here I have spent at sea. I rock now, when I am on land, and I've come to like that. I'm ill at ease on the land and free and laughing on the sea. My eye is always cast to the sea. I get a window seat on the plane and watch the sea from high above. I send a prayer down for Kostas and open my last box of Turkish delight.

I now understand the person who created Turkish delight. They must have lived near this glorious sea. For it is almost the texture of the delight itself. And the colours, the see through, glowing colours, and the long slow eating of it. This is a delight you can only know the truth of, after a long slow swim in these jellied waters.

## EIGHT

# Palaeo Man

### THE CAMINO

PORTO IS THE CITY OF CHIC COOL, OF TILED houses with wrought-iron balconies, of tiny cobbled streets and massive cathedrals. Seagulls call. This is a town where books are still cool, art is cool and fashion is cool. People wear blazers and leather shoes and clutch novels. Church bells ring on the quarter hour and wooden trams rattle down steep streets. Corner buildings are rounded like a ship's prow, and the river winds through to the sea.

I book myself into a hostel in the town square. I figure I had better get used to bunk rooms fast for that's all I will be using on this walk. The Catholic Church runs hostels for pilgrims walking the Camino, called albergues, with basic cheap bunks. There will be no luxury on this pilgrimage.

A drunken Saturday night happens outside my bunk room. Buses rumble, so do the snorers. There are no curtains and the street lights shine in, lighting up my face. There is no chance of oversleeping because there is no chance of sleeping.

I arrive at the steps of the cathedral at nine. The church bells chime as I enter. I smile. This must be auspicious, a very good sign. I am delighted with myself and with my timing. I pick up my pilgrims credential from the nun at the desk, get my first stamp, and sit for a while in the church, my pack at my feet, listening to the exultant organ and the choir singing praises to everything. The sun shines in the east window and I sit in radiant golden light.

Outside, the Cathedral Square is full of keen pilgrims. We all look at our maps. No one knows where to go. There are supposed to be yellow arrows pointing the way, but I see none. I figure I need to go down the hill, to the water. This is the coastal Camino, supposedly following the ocean all the way.

With a wave to the others, I go down the first narrow lane. It's a dead end. I try the next one, down some steep steps into a tangle of lanes and I am lost. Within five minutes of walking the Camino I am lost. It seems ridiculous to ask the way when I can still see the cathedral back up there.

I go back to the square. There is a new group of bewildered pilgrims there now. How can it be this hard to even start? My pack feels really heavy and my feet hurt and I'm lost and I'm still at the cathedral.

This is my first lesson in humility. I go back inside the cathedral, back to the nun at the desk, and ask the way. She marks the street on my map, saying, 'Always keep the water on your left.' She pats my hand and my cheek. She says, 'Buen Camino.'

My good cheer returns. There are kind people here, the sun is shining, I know the right way. And suddenly I do feel like a pilgrim. I walk out of this ancient town, on the right path, with my pack on my back and it's as if I walk out of the twenty-first century.

The path takes me alongside the river, wide and deep with a strong current. There are people fishing down there, on the muddy banks. They gather shellfish too, whelks, I think. Cars rattle over the cobbled streets on my right, and I rattle over the cobbled footpath. The cobbles are like sharp white teeth, and they hurt and hurt and hurt. I walk for three hours before I stop for a rest and a little cry.

Maybe I will take the bus. I have talked to others who have done the Camino, but when I really question them, it comes out that they have done the Camino in their car, in their nice car. The bus looks like a really good option right now.

There are three official ways of pilgrimage. You can ride a bike or a horse, or walk. In this modern fast world, a world full of people racing around with bucket lists, driving the Camino is a sure way of getting another thing ticked off the list. Sure, you can't get a 'compostela', a certificate from the church at the end if you drive it, but they assert, 'I don't need validation from anyone, let alone the church.'

It takes a long time to get out of Porto and its suburbs. They stretch right along the coastline. Weather-stained concrete boxes rise high, a disaster of twentieth-century cheap architecture. 'Look to the left,' becomes my motto. To the left is the Atlantic, in all its wild green glory. Steep beaches, rocky outcrops, golden sand, miles and miles and miles of green.

Mediating the middle ground between high rises and the sea are pohutukawa trees. Trees from home. The path is lined with them. Red flowers overhang, red flower needles scatter at my feet. I walk under them all day and I am grateful for their shade and their company.

It gets really hot and I learn my second lesson. Only fools start late. Only fools sit in the golden light of the church for way too long, thinking they are special and lucky. The path is the thing, and knowing how to walk the path is the most important thing. To escape the heat, the traffic, the bustle, I need to slip out of town before dawn. In the cool dark. All is lost for late starters.

I stop in an albergue in Labruge for the night. I lie down and pull the sheet up over my face, my only privacy in this room with 30 other beds in it. I shake quite a bit. I have walked 15 miles today; I have another 280 miles in front of me. It seems impossible.

The day isn't over, though, I still have to eat. This town has no cafés. There are some back the way I came but I can't bear to go back. 'No extra steps,' I whisper. That's my deal with myself, my way of self-care. Yes, I will push my body to do this, but I won't do extra, not one step. It's sort of comforting, and also defiant, this secret deal I have. There is a little shop selling cans of beans next door. I buy two, one for dinner, one for breakfast.

I tie a scarf around my eyes to block out the light, for there are no curtains. Sleep comes swiftly. I know the room is full of snorers and rustlers, but that all fades away. The biggest blessing of the day comes at the end, when I get to escape it.

Until 5am. Suddenly everyone is up. Everyone has 10 plastic bags they need to open and then reopen. Everyone has a water bottle that they kick over in the dark. Everyone has phones that buzz and light up the room. Everyone needs to walk to the end of the room and back 50 times while they pack their packs. It is pointless to stay in bed. So I get up and kick my water bottle over too. I limp around, rustle my bags, and load up the day's map.

I examine the blister that covers the whole ball of my left foot, put some plasters on it and hope for the best. The word among the other pilgrims is that today's path is all boardwalk. My spirits rise. I am up early, I have beans for breakfast, I have plasters on my feet and I have a wooden path.

The boardwalk makes all the difference, but my feet have been badly damaged by yesterday's cobblestones. I can feel them, swollen and tingling. They don't seem to flex any more. They are just wooden clumps attached to my legs. My walk changes to accommodate them, and I have to sort of slide them along, just an inch above the ground. I turn into a shuffler. I tell myself, 'It doesn't matter how I look,' and, 'It's not a race, this Camino thing, this life thing.'

But it is a race. Beds fill up quickly and there aren't many pilgrim albergues on this Camino. It's not the wildly popular Camino Francis up in the north, with a rich choice of accommodation. This is the way of St James, and only gets 20 per cent of the walkers. The infrastructure really isn't here, and those 20 per cent are on a race this fine morning.

I can't join in the race, even if I want to, with my new shuffle. All day I look out for places to sleep, just in case. Under the boardwalk in the sand looks like the best option.

The boardwalk becomes my good friend for the next three days. It has yellow arrows showing me the way, and it also has the number to call for an ambulance. I do think of doing the Camino by ambulance. It makes me laugh, to think of saying, 'Yeah, I did the Camino. By ambulance, it's the only way. It's life changing.'

The boardwalk keeps me safe, and it keeps me close to the coast, away from the new towns, away from the ugliness. Concrete high rises face a difficult beach. It all looks hostile, wind whipped. Black mould grows on the concrete walls, and yellow streaks stain. The towns merge into one bleak high-rise strip of barren emptiness.

It gets to me, this lack of beauty. For a few days it gets to me, and then I start not noticing it any more. What I do notice are the old churches, the stone bridges, the old Roman roads, the forts guarding river mouths, the pagan mounds, the rock carvings. The wild, wild sea.

For what matters, what always matters is the path. The path underneath all this modernity. The path that has been walked for thousands of years. I connect into that and walk from ancient fort to ancient fort. And the thing is, underneath it all, I can feel it, the force and the rightness of this path. Modern life slips away.

I have my first miracle. I find that my wonderful black cat Cosmic isn't dead. He is here on this path. He appears on the tops of walls, in windows, down alleyways. I call out, 'Hey Cosmic, I see you.' I know, I really know that my cat comes with me. I see him when I am at my lowest, when I am tired or lost or hungry, and there he is, my big black cat. He isn't dead. He's just become more powerful!

There are a lot of friends to be had on this path. Anyone with a white scallop shell tied to their backpack is a willing friend, and there are plenty of us. During the day people mostly walk alone, for the Camino is all about finding your own pace. People are loath to disturb that. But once we arrive at the albergue, it's a social city. It's easy to connect because we all have everything in common.

At Povoa de Varzim I meet Lars. He cooks his dinner in the kitchen while I cook mine. He gives me his leftover tomatoes, and I give him half of my spinach.

He sees me hobbling to the table and takes a look at my feet for me. 'Plantar fasciitis, that's what this looks like,' he says, 'easy to get from walking on uneven cobblestones.'

I talk about that first day walking out of Porto for hours on cobblestones and my feet never recovering. 'That's why I took the train out to the boardwalk,' he says.

I didn't know trains were an option for day one of a pilgrimage. I want to joke about taking the ambulance on day one but I'm not sure if he would laugh at that so I don't. He knows some stretches to help my feet. So we do that, on the carpet by the sofa. He says he will see me on the path, but I doubt it. He is very tall, his legs are long and his feet work.

I shuffle out of town early in the morning, in the dark, and I wish I had a cloak. I need it to fit into this landscape. I need a rough grey cloak, with a big hood. Already my clothes have turned to rags. Modern clothes don't work properly here and I need something that can be a blanket, a towel, a dress and a picnic rug.

The path winds us through all the ancient sites, both Catholic and pagan, for this was a pilgrimage in ancient times too. Neolithic times the signs say, way before Christianity was even a thing. I like to think of the stone-age people on long distance travel excursions, carrying their lunch like me, tired and dirty, just like me.

I sit on some black rocks, high up on the headland, an

old pagan ritual site, so the sign says, and eat my lunch. I know things have happened here, important things, I can feel it. I lie down on the rocks, out of the wind, and let their warmth ease into me.

And I hear it again, that far-off singing. I lie there astonished, barely breathing, while the rocks sing, high and distant. It is the same singing I heard in Guinea. I thought I would never hear that again, that it was drum magic. Maybe it really is my own ears, opening up to other things. Amadou was right. Once your ears start to work properly, listening gives you a doorway into something else. And here it is again.

This time the voices are coming from these rocks, deep in the earth. I breathe the song from the rock and into me and I realise there is something else happening on this path. There is magic here.

And there is Lars, striding up the boardwalk. His blond hair tousled by the wind, his smile wide. I sit up, give him a wave and he comes to join me. I am surprised to see him behind me, with those long legs. 'I stopped for lunch,' he says, 'and it took a long time to cook my meat. I eat like the ancient ones, the Palaeolithics.'

It turns out that Lars has had three lunches already, two vegetable lunches and one with a big meaty bone. 'And I have to stop for the berries too,' he says. 'The blackberries are great along here.' I have been stopping for the berries as well; there are so many big ripe ones that it's hard to walk past. 'I'm a natural gatherer,' he says, 'I'm Palaeolithic Man.'

Lars tells me he is walking the Camino for the old pagan path, not the Christian one that was laid down on top of it. I almost tell him about the singing. I almost ask him to lie down on the rocks with me to see if he hears it too. But then I stop. My words run out and I feel too modern, too logical to talk about something as strange as singing deep in a rock. Even to Palaeolithic Man.

We walk a little way together, but Lars is in good physical shape and I am not. He likes to go fast, and I say I like to go slow. I don't like going slow, but I have no choice. I watch him lope off into the distance, and I sigh and tell myself again, 'It's not a race this Camino thing.'

At Esposende the boardwalks finish. It's back to cobblestones or concrete. Both make my feet scream. I stop at the closest albergue and get the last bed in a 40-bunk bed room. People are lying down, silent, sheets pulled over their faces, bodies turned to the wall. The air is weighted with weariness. I have a top bunk. I have no idea how I'm going to get up there, so I heave my pack up and take my body outside to lie on the earth.

It's nice out, under the trees. It's a bit damp but that means nothing. My feet throb as if a thousand bees have been at them. They are covered in a red prickly rash, and it seems now I fit a size 13 shoe, not a size 9. That could be my problem. I have shoes four sizes too small.

I know I need to wash, both my body and my clothes. It's hard to stand up, though, once I'm down. I lie on the grass for three hours, shaking. Tears leak out of my eyes, so I fling my arm across them and pretend I am just resting, like everyone else.

I know there will be no hot water left, there never is, by the time I can stand up again. Cleanliness is not as important as rest. I only have two changes of clothes; both are filthy. When I can stand again, I limp down to the shop for food.

It's a small shop. Mostly, it has empty shelves, but I find some beans and some onions.

That night the bunk room shakes with snoring. Suddenly I can't stand it, the aching feet, no sleep, beans every dinner, the sweat, the shaking, never being clean.

Communal living seems terrible, and this walk is the worst thing in the world. I think back to Kostas in Turkey, to jumping off the boat, to all that joy, and I berate myself for leaving. Here I am exhausted and sore, and I could be there, in jellied delight. I fume all night at snorers who book themselves into bunk rooms, and who hog the bottom bunks. I whip myself into a foul mood.

In the morning I thrash about early, hoping to wake the snorers, to give them a taste of their own medicine. But nothing will wake them. I let my water bottle fall from the top bunk. Three times. I rustle my big plastic bag, I bang my pack down, but nothing. And I am so, so angry. I hate everyone.

I know I need a rest day, but I can't rest here. I hate it here. I will do a small day's walk over the hill and stay there. These snorers will do a massive day and walk out of my life. I will never have to see them, or more importantly sleep with them ever again.

It's a pity I'm in such a bad mood because this walk is lovely. It's up over a hill and through a river valley, and the best thing of all is that it's through forest. Mostly it's eucalypts, which I find very strange, being an Australian thing and here I am in Portugal, but there are enough other trees shining through. Cork oaks, chestnuts, things that would have been here forever. And it's truly magic to be in a forest, after days and days of high-rise towns. The branches hang down low over the track, and shrubs push in from the sides. All is green, dappled, quiet.

And yay for me, because this albergue is the most wonderful of them all. It has wooden built-in bunks that don't squeak when you turn over. It's small, new and the best thing of all is that there is only one other pilgrim here. She chooses a bunk at the far end and we both pretend we are alone.

Maria runs this albergue. She's a volunteer and has come early to light the candles in front of the statues. She believes in the path so much that she dedicates her days to helping pilgrims. She sits behind the wooden desk and slowly registers me in her book.

Then she reaches down and pulls a bottle of port out of the desk cupboard. 'The secretary needs some wine,' she says, 'and I think the pilgrim does too.' We drink our wine in the sun and she tells me about her dancing group, her cleaning job, and her love for God.

In the afternoon I go down to the river. It is surrounded by trees and has a little stone slab bridge. There is no one here. I wade through the arches, through the shadows, where eels may live, and I swim in the water falling from the rocks. It is freezing, but it is what my body needs. I float downstream, then hang on to low branches and let the current take me.

Getting back is hard, for the current is strong. Still, it's good to use my arm muscles, and to give my feet a rest. I don't even try to kick, I just let my legs float out behind me. The cold water does wonders for my feet. For the first time in days, I can even flex them. I think of all those healing waters, the sacred streams and fountains that people still pilgrimage to. And I think I have just had my second miracle. The miraculous foot flex.

The river and the afternoon's rest make me feel better. Even though I'm way behind, I realise there is nothing to be behind in. I have no planned end date; I just got caught up in other people's races.

I slowly sink into the strangeness of this journey. And it is strange, to walk into a bustling city with a backpack on, to follow the yellow arrows spray painted onto gutters and lampposts, while the fashionable have lunch and go to their offices. I walk past shops full of high fashion but I can't go in, not in sweaty rags and a pack. I don't even go inside cafés; I eat out on the pavement. Fashionable towns bewilder me now. I am extra careful in towns not to get lost, but I still get lost in Viana do Castelo.

This town is on the other side of a wide estuary. A long, high bridge takes me in. Cars speed past and the pedestrian path is a little clip-on afterthought. Underneath, trains rumble through. There is space for everyone on this bridge. The pedestrian part is a bit precarious, though. I hold on to the rail with my right hand, and my hat with my left and try not to look down. It feels like I am dangling out over the side of the world.

This is a big town, probably a city. There are underpasses, roundabouts and suddenly no arrows. But I do have friends, in this place where I know no one. Anyone who walks this path with a shell on their backpack is a friend. I return to the last arrow. I sit down. I wait for a friend to come along.

From the restaurant opposite I see someone waving. It is my friend Lars. I shuffle over the road and sit with him while he eats his second lunch of the day. A meaty bone in soup. He picks it up in his hands, 'Palaeo style,' he says, 'no utensils back then.' He enjoys ripping it up, biting deep into the flesh. He says he's starving, he's always starving.

I say, 'Why don't you have rice or potatoes with it? That would help fill you up.'

He leans over. 'No grains, Sarah, I live on meat, vegetables, nuts and berries. Just like our ancestors did.'

He tells me he has been spending time at the ancient sites. 'I just sit there, hoping to hear something, feel something,' he says. 'This path makes me feel connected, like I'm right back there. It's like I'm living in dreamtime.'

His real destination is Finisterre, further on from Santiago where I am heading. 'That was the end of the world to the ancients,' he says. 'That's where I'm going. They burnt their clothes by the ocean at the end of the world, facing the setting sun. That's what I'm going to do.'

There is much talk among pilgrims of why they are doing this path. Many talk about releasing burdens, about lightening the load of their lives. Physical things are released along the way too. Pilgrims leave their shampoo behind, their novel, their spare shoes. Anything to lighten their pack. I leave my towel. I figure when I do get to wash, I can just dry in the wind.

Most people don't discuss what their actual burdens are. That is for individual contemplation on the road, or in the dark of the bunk bed. Some people are planning on releasing them at the cathedral, on the shoulders of St James. Some are intending to release them at Finisterre, into the sea.

I spend a lot of the walking time thinking of my burdens. Those things that I just can't shake off. I figure I need to be as precise as possible at the moment of release. It's not going to be enough to plead to the wind, the sea, or the ear of St James, 'Please, please, just take away all the bad stuff.'

Through the restaurant window we can see a lot of people getting lost here. From my seat I can see the yellow arrow is painted on the curb, but people are used to finding them on lampposts. They look around bewildered for a while, then there is an exclamation, a wave of an arm, 'There it is,' and they are off again.

It's fun following the arrows, the clues through these cities, and it does make me feel that I'm part of something bigger. We join the trail again, but Lars is ahead of me by the time I have crossed the road. 'See you tonight maybe,' he yells over his shoulder.

On the sides of the road, in chinks carved out of walls, are little shrines. They have a picture of Jesus or Mary behind a grille. There are candles to be lit, prayers to be said, just walking along the footpath. Sometimes, at a crossroads or in a spare triangle of land there is a statue, St Anthony is popular in these parts, being Portuguese himself. Churches, saints and shrines mark the path as well as the yellow arrows. I realise that if I do get lost again, I just have to go to the oldest church in town and pick up the trail from its front door.

I start to love the churches. They are cool and quiet and the perfect place for a rest. Public space is not really a thing out here in the countryside so the church and its grounds become the public space for us pilgrims. We gather there, compare maps, discuss where we are stopping for the night, where we might have lunch.

Pilgrims seem to be the only ones at church. When they are locked, we sit outside. They become our places. We start praying there too. We pray over our burdens; we look at our blisters and pray for strength. I start praying for a bottom bunk.

The countryside puzzles me. My new European friends talk about this countryside and how expansive and beautiful it is. I spend a long time waiting to get into the countryside before I realise they are talking about what we are actually in right now. To me, this seems like normal houses and gardens in the suburbs.

The others talk about the wonderful forests too, but they are actually eucalypt plantations. These are trees that burn fast. In the hot afternoons I worry about forest fires and I imagine these trees exploding into fire as I walk through.

There is a pilgrim who walks elusively in front of me. I think it's a man, but I only catch glimpses, so I can't be sure. He wears all white and carries a tall wooden walking stick. He looks completely Zen. He is thin, toned, calm, spiritual.

I want to look like him, but I know I don't. Still, I think a stick might help. I don't want those modern aluminium poles people use, but I would like a nice wooden stick.

There are walking sticks for sale in the towns, but I definitely don't want to buy one, I want to find one. I'm sure my Zen man has found his. The Camino books I have read talk about 'the stick finding you'. So I shuffle around in the forest, off the path, poking under trees. I call out to my stick, hoping it might hear me, might find me.

That night Lars is in the albergue. He has a bottom bunk, being an early arrival. He is lying down, resting when I shuffle in. There are only top bunks left at this late stage of the day. But Lars jumps up, 'This is your bunk, here at the bottom. I have been saving it for you; I prefer the top,' he says.

I think Lars is the most generous man I have ever met. I could fall in love with this man who saves me a bottom bunk.

He cooks us dinner too. He stands up and stirs the pot while I sit down and arrange the forks. It's not that hard to cook dinner though. Everything we have we put together in one pot. He has beans, I have a carrot left over from lunch. We eat with forks straight out of the pot. No extra steps has become no extra work.

I tell Lars about my stick problem: how hard it is to attract the right stick into my life. He looks incredulous and says, 'Do you really think a stick will make you look Zen?'

I look down at myself, my stained long pants, my stained long-sleeved shirt, my clunky shoes, my straw hat, my swollen body bursting through under it all. 'Yes,' I say.

At Caminha the path takes me inland, up the river to Valenca and over the bridge into Spain. A momentous day, I think, and indeed it turns out to be so. The path follows the river. It is shaded with huge trees: cork oaks, beech and chestnut. It's only a thin strip of forest, maybe 300 metres wide, and I can still see houses just over there, but I pretend I don't.

I walk quietly, hoping to see a stag in the shafts of early-morning sun. It feels like that is entirely possible. The river is alive with fish, their backs breaking the water in a black mass. This is the first place that I have felt could almost be wild. I walk alone. I feel like a pilgrim, on a mission to relieve my burden, slipping quietly through an ancient forest.

There is a high stone bridge that crosses the path into Spain, and suddenly everything is different. The bridge leads straight into the ancient town of Tui. Everything is loud here. I find myself in the middle of 300 shouting school children, all with packs and walking sticks. They pour out of the train station and jostle up through the narrow stone streets.

Tui is 100 kilometres from Santiago. In order to gain a Compostela you have to walk at least the last hundred kilometres of the path. This is an important starting point for many people. New, excited pilgrims are everywhere.

I trudge up to the cathedral square, sweat running down my back, dazed by all the noise. Buskers play on the cathedral steps: there are bagpipes, violins, singers. Stallholders rush up and tie ribbons on my pack, on my wrist. They shout, 'Buen Camino,' and throw their arms around me in a hug. There are T-shirts, badges, headbands, walking sticks. It seems the tourist trail starts here.

I walk into the cathedral and walk out again straight away, shocked. It costs to go into this church. That doesn't feel right, for a tired pilgrim to pay to sit in a church. I sit on the steps instead and look at the party happening in the square.

For it seems I am in a giant party. I have arrived on a day of great celebration. The people are having a fiesta to celebrate the good relations between Spain and Portugal over the sharing of the river. Fireworks and music are happening in both Tui and Valenca. There are loud booms and people in national dress running through the streets.

These towns do have much to celebrate. The river they share is beautiful. It is clean, seething with fish, birds, insects, and is heavily wooded on both sides. It's easy to see how relations could get tense here. The river is not very wide, and a shout from one side can be heard from the other. But they have managed, and tonight they celebrate.

There is no sleep to be had. My albergue is in the cathedral square, the main stage of the party. But I lie and rest my body, and I don't mind the no sleep. Not when the celebration is over something as vital as an alive river.

I leave at dawn. I slip down through the dark streets and into the surrounding forest. I'm in Galicia now, a deeply mystical, Celtic region of Spain and the seventh Gallic nation. This is Palaeolithic country; this is what Lars has been looking forward to. There are petroglyphs, dolmens and Celtic hill forts.

The forest feels old, as much of it as I can see in the dim morning light, and soft magic is in the air. I sit on a small stone slab bridge quietly watching the early sun shaft the river below.

And then I hear them. The 300 school children from yesterday. They are in good cheer, for it is day one for them. By the noise they make I think they have multiplied in the night. Maybe another miracle on the path?

It's nice to hear kids singing, but it's also nice to hear the forest breathing. After the celebrations last night, I am a little tired of singing. I go off the path, behind a tree, and sit and wait for them to pass.

There are a lot of pilgrims on the path today; it seems many started their Camino yesterday. I wait for a long time behind that tree and watch pilgrims walk by. It's easy to tell the new people – they are clean. They chat and laugh and call out with their friends. It seems the longer I walk the path the quieter I become. I have become wide eyed, wild haired, dirty and silent.

Round the table that night talk is of an alternative route, 'The Variante Espiritual'. People seem extra keen on this after walking with the school kids all day. 'It's spiritual, right?' says Peter. 'That means quiet, right?'

Anna says, 'We have to do it. It's harder and longer, and that will put them off.'

Lars nods, 'I'm sure the kids won't be on that path.'

We all decide that's the path for us. The path of the variant.

I stay the night in Combarro, a town famous for its ceremonial witch sites. The town is built on basalt, right at the edge of the estuary, and stone paths weave around outcrops of black rock. On top of those outcrops large stone crosses have been erected in an effort to ward off witches. Mary is on one side, facing the sea, and Jesus on the other, facing the land. Combarro is full of these old pagan sites that Christians have laid their saints over.

A mountain looms behind the town. It is covered in eucalypt trees, and I know tomorrow's path will be a shady one, even though it will be steep. I try not to look at it too much; I don't want to be reminded of what is in front of me.

I walk into the square for dinner and there is Lars, tucking into a bone at a café.

Anna and Peter are there too. Lars is full of admiration for this place. 'I feel right at home here,' he says. 'This is my place.' He plans on sitting out on one of the rocky outcrops all night. 'I can feel them here, the ancient ones, I'm going to connect with them tonight!' he exclaims.

We leave Lars with a little pile of seeds and nuts, sitting on some high black stones and looking out to sea. Back at the albergue we play 'Saints: the Card Game'. It is strange to laugh and slap down cards of saints performing miracles when those very things are what I pray about during the day. It's fun, though, playing this game with my new friends. When we pass by the stones in the morning dark, Lars is still there, his eyes wild, his nuts and seeds gone. He shouts out as we pass, 'Astonishing! Astonishing!'

The mountain doesn't look so bad in the morning, mostly because it's so dark I can't see the top. I tighten my pack a bit and settle into a slow trudge. And it's not that bad actually. Maybe I really am fitter these days. I think of how amazing I'm going to look when I walk into Santiago. Fit and strong and lean. Even Zen, once my stick finds me.

'Shuffle into Santiago,' a voice in my head says. 'Don't forget you still do that.'

The sun rises, and there are grand views down the coast. It's nice being up this high. I try to focus on that, and how amazingly fit and strong I am, while the sweat slides down my back and my feet swell.

I find a patch of blackberries so I stop for them, throwing my pack on the ground while I eat. Lars lopes up. 'You found us breakfast!' he exclaims and joins me. I notice his feet. He has really strange shoes on. They look like chain mail and are sort of tied on.

'Cool shoes,' I say.

'Yes!' he exclaims, 'these are my Palaeo barefoot shoes.' He lifts them up to show me the little paw pads on the bottom, for his toes and heels. 'Perfect for today, the path is earth today, so the book says.'

I look at them for a while. They do seem quite a thing to have been carrying all this time. I say, 'Why don't you just go barefoot?'

He is puzzled at that, 'Barefoot?' he repeats, 'but the earth is dirty. With these shoes I get to stay clean, and besides, I don't get prickles.' I look at the path in front of us. It is earth and there are no prickles. 'I have all the Palaeo gear, Sarah,' he says, 'this is my life now.'

I want to ask about a cloak. If he has one and if I can borrow it. I want to ask him if I should catch some insects for him, if worms are okay, and what is his stance on road kill – is it the equivalent of lion kill? I want to really laugh, and really tease. But I don't, because Lars is lovely and he's enjoying himself, and he saves me the bottom bunks.

Halfway up the mountain there is a sign for petroglyphs. Lars is really excited. He grabs my hand and we scramble up the steep path off to the right. And there it is, a big circle spiral carved in a slab of rock. I run my hand over it, brushing the leaves away, feeling into the grooves. It feels strange and powerful to be running my hand over such ancient art.

Then we see more on the rocks below, a long animal, three running deer, maybe a stick figure. 'A hunter!' exclaims Lars. 'One of my people!' We sit there on the ground among the art of our ancestors. We eat almonds out of a packet and talk about them. 'I can feel them everywhere here,' whispers Lars, and strangely I sort of can too.

There is a monastery, way up here in the hills, that we visit on the way to the albergue. It is an old walled complex full of serenity. It has a gift shop too, with a monk behind the counter. He is radiant. Love seems to pour out his eyes.

Lars tells him about the petroglyphs, and his connection with the ancients last night, and the monk nods and laughs and blesses us both. He invites us to the evening service tonight that will be full of singing and joy.

I buy a bottle of eucalyptus liquor. It does seem an odd thing to have in a church shop, but it looks like part of the industry up here; the nuns make it, and they make soap. I would like to buy soap as well, but a whole bar of soap is a luxury item for me now. Besides, it would be a waste, seeing I have no towel to go with it, and seeing I don't wash.

We drink the eucalyptus liquor together, sitting in the long grass outside. We drink the whole bottle because neither of us wants to carry it tomorrow. Suddenly going to church seems like the best option in the world.

And it is. The monk is right. There is much singing and there is much joy. At the end of the service all the pilgrims are called to the front. We circle around, and he lays his hands on our heads and blesses us one by one as the nuns sing.

I feel special and golden and loved. He whispers to me, 'I hope you find your way, and that your burdens are lifted.' My eyes prick as I think of all those burdens I am carrying and all those paths I keep getting lost on.

The famous 'Water and Stone' track leads us out of town in the morning. Lars leaves early, but I don't want to walk this track in the dark, so I start late, and I'm pleased I do. For this is a real forest, with ferns, mosses, massive beech trees. The path is shady all the way, and seeing I am late it is all mine.

I wander down the path in a diffused green light. The trees are so dense that I don't see the houses that I know are just out there. I walk in mediaeval magic. Old stone steps follow the river as it gushes and tumbles. There are water courses, stone houses, and ancient things. And I wish I had asked Lars about that cloak.

In the afternoon the path turns from shaded forest to the white glare of town; the earth turns back to cobblestones. My heart sinks. It's a hard slog with miles and miles of disaster for my feet.

My black cat Cosmic appears a lot, just in front of me. I think of him and how he pulled the family together. I have a little cry, for the alive Cosmic that I loved. For Billy and Ellowyn patting him by the fire. For his purr.

That night there is no one I know in the albergue. Lars has walked on to the next town, along with Peter and Anna, but I know I can't make it that far. I arrive late. I shake in my top bunk until I go to sleep.

The next morning the path goes up the river by boat. 'Ha,' I think, 'Camino by boat!' but apparently this is official and sanctioned, for this is the way St James' bones were smuggled up through the country, in secret by his two friends.

I get into a rubber speedboat and we race up the river. Little towns flow by, and big stone crosses, erected right down at the river's edge. It is surprisingly moving. It feels like the perfect place to smuggle the bones of your friend to a safe place. I would choose this place too.

It's hard to join back into the main Camino path, after the variant. There are lots of people, big albergues, and I can't find my friends. The closer I get to Santiago the more people there are. Santiago is where my attention is focused, but the closer I get the further away it feels. There seem to be days and days of shuffling in the heat.

On my last night I stop just 10 kilometres out of Santiago. I think it will be an easy morning walk and I should be there in time for breakfast. It is not an easy morning's walk; it is hard, like all the other mornings. I leave at 5, in the dark. I have to use my torch to see the arrows. I barely notice the surroundings. I just lock into the arrows. They are what I live for.

I see the spires of the cathedral through the pine trees. I stop and have a quick catch of breath that turns into a quick sob. But I have no time for a real cry here. I shuffle on. The cathedral is the thing now, that's what's pulling me. I have to get there.

And then the path spills me out onto a busy street. There are high rises, cars, pedestrians, flash shops and suddenly there are no more arrows. I'm in Santiago. I'm so, so close, but I can't see the cathedral, and I don't know my way. This path is consistent in its unfolding of the truth, 'As it was in the beginning, so it shall be at the end'.

I can't bear to ask the way so I walk on, through narrow alleyways and high stones. I figure that all roads must lead to the cathedral in this town.

And suddenly the alleyway spills me out into the cathedral square.

I am here.

I am here.

Everything hurts but I am here. I am the slowest, but I am still here. I barely know who I am any more, but I am still here.

I take my pack off, I sink down into the stones and I weep.

Around me the square is busy. There are other pilgrims too, lying on the stones, crying. And there are tour buses, shops, buskers and a jangle of people. Here we all are, at the end of things.

I haven't finished, though, as there are still things to do. So I shoulder my pack again and walk down to the Pilgrims Office, my pilgrims credential in my hand. It is full of stamps: 300 miles worth of stamps. I join the queue of bone-weary people, tear-stained, dirty people. We line up outside the chapel and we don't speak. We have no words any more.

When it is my turn I hand over my credential. The registrar is delighted with me. He reads my stamps out aloud, all the places I have stayed. He says, 'This is a hard path, you have done well to walk this.' He writes my name on my Compostela and adds my name and nationality to his register. My nationality will be announced in the cathedral the next morning, and I will be added to the long list of pilgrims. I cry again. It seems Santiago is the crying city.

I can barely stand and I'm so tired. My feet hurt, my eyes are swollen, I haven't eaten and it's already noon. But I want to go into the cathedral. I have never queued to get into church before, but in Santiago that's what happens every day for Mass.

Inside, huge gilt angels fly up near the ceiling, bending their heads so they don't hit the roof. They carry the chariot of St James, and he sits there in the middle of it all, larger than life, splendid in his golden massiveness. Victorious. Strong enough to shoulder everyone's burdens.

I take my pack off and sit at a wooden pew near the back.

It is a relief to be sitting. I try to stand for the songs, along with everyone else, but I find I can't. Not even if I hold on to the pew in front.

I ease my shoes off and feel the wooden prayer plank. It feels cool and smooth on the skin between my plasters. I cry again, but I have nothing to blow my nose on or wipe my eyes with. Except the old stained shirt I am wearing. I use that.

It's a challenge to stand up to leave. I want to sleep where I am; this pew would be fine. But I find some food, I manage a shower, and then I go to bed.

I spend the whole of the next day crying. I go to the Pilgrim's Chapel where they play 'The Beatitudes of the Pilgrim'. I sit at a pew on the side, I lean into the wall, bend my head and cry. I cry in my bunk. I cry having coffee, walking through the square, in the tourist shops. Everywhere.

I go back to the cathedral square, sit down at the back and watch this day's pilgrims arrive. Small, covered alleyways lead into the square, and the bagpiper plays in one of them. The pilgrims walk in and fall to the ground in front of the cathedral. They are dirty and exhausted and do not get up. They lie there for hours, hats over their faces.

Sometimes they arrive in groups or pairs and give hugs and loud shouts, but after a while they find an alone space. They find quiet corners; they go to the edge. Alone. They cry alone. Heads on knees. They close their eyes and think of what they have done.

And around us busloads of fashionable tourists that have flown in for the day buy shells and sticks so they too can look like pilgrims. But they don't lie down in the dust and cry. They shop.

I watch two girls hobble in, one with her arm around the shoulders of the other. She has a stick in her other hand and can barely touch one of her feet to the ground. They are both sobbing, and I don't think either of them will make it into the square. But they do, just. At the entrance, just inside, facing the cathedral they crumple to the ground.

The waiter at the café I have lunch at tells me he loves living here. He says, 'This place cracks my heart open every day.'

He is right. Santiago cracks its heart open for these limping pilgrims.

In the evening I go to Mass again. This time I can stand. The priest says there will be a pilgrims' tour afterwards, so I stay for that, although not many of us do. He leads us to the centre of the outside cloisters where he has a black cauldron. We are given black paper, symbolic of the burdens we want released. He lights a fire in the cauldron and he sings as one by one we burn our paper.

It is a powerful ceremony, welcome in its honouring of tradition. I know we can't all burn our clothes at the end of the Camino, for the pollution would be overwhelming. There are a thousand people a day completing this pilgrimage. But the burning of paper is enough.

The cathedral is under renovations, so we can't see all of it, but the priest guides us around, giving us a history lesson. He explains the carvings, shows us the touching post. We go up under the angels and we all say our prayers aloud, in whatever language we have. Then we go down into the crypt to see the bones of St James.

The priest explains that no one knew the bones were here. A monk heard the rocks singing and saw bright lights right on this hill. The place was excavated and found to contain bones of three men: two older men, who they assume were his friends from the boat, and the bones of a man who had died by beheading. St James himself.

If someone had told me this story before I had walked the Camino I would have scoffed. 'Yeah, no way,' I would have said. But now I believe it all. I have heard the rocks singing too. I believe in singing rocks.

This cathedral feels alive, as alive as the river at Tui had felt, and it also feels like it belongs to me, or rather, I belong to it. All I want to do is stay in it all night and receive its blessings.

The statue of St James sits golden and glorious behind the altar, on a high throne. There are narrow dark stairs behind him. I climb them. I wrap my arms around him from behind. I lay my head on his broad shoulders.

And there, finally, I lay down my burdens.


There are still two days before my flight. I hang out in town, around the cathedral shops and cafés. I know lots of people in town; I have walked with them for weeks.

I met Lars in the coffee shop down the alley from my albergue. I have chocolate churros, and he just has chocolate. He is heading out to Finisterre on the bus that afternoon. 'Come with me,' he says, 'let's light a raging fire and dance at the end of the world.'

I ask him if he has done any ceremony, any burden release, in Santiago. 'No, I am saving it for the fire,' he says.

I realise that our timing is wrong, and there is something under that that is wrong too. One of the burdens I had released was to stop pretending and stop pleasing others. If I went with Lars, I would be doing a pretend ceremony, and I would be doing what he wanted me to do.

'Come with me,' he says again, 'be my Palaeolithic Woman.'


Santiago is my favourite European city now. It feels like my end goal. The Mythical Kingdom that I got to spend four magic days in as its pilgrim. It feels like I belong to this city. I walked for this city and for this saint without even knowing what I was walking for. When I started, I didn't know anything.

Maybe at the end of our lives we get to our own Santiagos. Where we are surprised and enchanted and weep. For we did not know what we were doing, but somehow we did it. And we find that we have always been walking towards grace, on this long, long path.

# NINE

# The Passport Hunter

I NEED SOMEWHERE TO REST, WHERE I CAN HEAL MY feet and feel into what really happened on the Camino. My brother works in Liverpool. He has a flat there overlooking the Mersey that is free for the summer while he is on holiday. I didn't think I would have to use it, but now I am grateful for his offer. I know I will have a proper bed, a kitchen all to myself and solitude.

I arrive in Manchester, catch the train to Liverpool and walk from the train station to the flat. Still with my pack on, still on my Camino. I climb two flights of stairs and unlock the door to his empty house.

My first job is food. My brother left two weeks ago and the cupboards are bare. I empty the Camino gear out of my pack, put it straight back on my back and limp off to the supermarket.

There is a little lane, a short cut up the hill that my brother has told me about. I take that. Breathing is difficult in this lane. I didn't expect the piles of dog poo that sting my throat. I didn't expect having to shuffle through rubbish in this prosperous modern city. There are signs warning of heavy fines for dog poo, but it seems we don't care about that here.

I work out that I can hold my breath for 16 seconds. I walk as fast as I can, head down, finding a safe path through. At the corner by the stairs, a city hire bike lies wrecked.

At the top of the stairs there is a railing to stop people falling down the steep bank. Drink cans, food containers and plastic bags are piled up here. Here, on the corner people must eat hard and fast, and fling the evidence over the railings. The hideout of the secret eaters' club is here. The whole suburb is in on it too, judging by the rubbish heap. Even the blackberry is stopped by the pile. There is no chance of any rain reaching the ground over this dump of plastic. We have our own mini desertification starting.

I look around and realise I may not be living in a very good suburb. I may be part of the downtrodden, the poor, the angry and the sullen.

The shops on the high street have roller doors pulled down, black rusty ones with graffiti. The pub is the only thing open and it is open all day. I walk through streets of grim terrace houses. There are hanging baskets filled with grubby plastic flowers over front doors. Signs saying 'No Ball Games' are nailed to walls. The little boys play war instead. They have plastic guns and play at marching up and down the street and shooting each other, while the little girls paint their nails on the doorstep.

Pyjamas are the dress code. I am overdressed, even in my old Camino clothes. There is a small park at the top of the hill, but only those with dogs use it, those with big meaty dogs. It would work if I cut across the park to the supermarket, but I don't.

'You all right, love?' they ask me at the supermarket. The people have banded together in a sort of tribe, and just by being here I am included. We gather around the shelves where the almost expired food is on sale. We shake our heads over the terrible price of things, even the almost expired things. The checkout girl goes really slow. She sighs and tells me she would like to be on holiday, but she can't afford one this year.

The walk home is difficult, even though it's downhill. I have bought as much food as I can carry and my pack is the heaviest it has ever been, even heavier than my first day of the Camino. The weight of it all pushes me into the concrete.

It is worth it, though, for I have enough food to not leave the flat for a week. Even though my brother is not here, it sort of feels like he is. I cocoon myself in his flat and his stuff, and it is the most home-like feeling I have had all year.

It gives me time to think about what just happened on the Camino. I know something has shifted inside of me, something big. I think St James and I really did work a piece of magic. Even though I am exhausted I know inside me I am well. My feet hurt, but my heart is light. I feel inside me for the bitterness, the shame, the old stomach churn. There is nothing there. Those burning feelings that have travelled with me for so long aren't there any more.

St James must really have them.

There is a different feeling too, a feeling like now I've only just begun. Even though I finished walking, it feels like I'm at the start now of a real pilgrimage. I don't know what that is, but I do know there is now space inside for something else to happen, that the journey's end is really the journey's beginning.

My brother has asked his friend Laura to check up on me. She lives in the flat three doors down and remarkably is a physiotherapist. She takes a look at my feet, gives me some stretches to do and a spiky ball to roll under them, but mostly she prescribes bare feet and rest. So that is what I do. I sleep, stretch my feet, talk to Billy and Ellowyn on the phone, and look out across the Mersey.

The flat hovers right over the river. There is only a thin footpath separating the building from the water. The river is so close I could fish off the balcony. But it makes me want to cry. It's a brown swirling sludge of pollution, a post-industrial mess. At high tide the water surges and pushes against the sea wall. It feels angry, this river. Things float down it, containers and plastic bags filled with rubbish.

At low tide I lean over the balcony and take an inventory of what is below me in the sludge: three tyres, a supermarket trolley, eleven road cones, coils of thick rope, long industrial pipes, and oddly angled, unidentifiable things. It looks like there is an abandoned car out there too; I can only see its roof and windows as the rest sits under water.

I lean out and look left up the Mersey, to Runcorn. Bright orange flames from smoke stacks rise into the sky. Still, this is happening. Still, things are burning up there.

The Festival Gardens are really close to my flat. I imagine being barefoot on the grass and how lovely that would feel, so I set off along the river path. Dogs are allowed off leash on this path, and every day there are problems, altercations, shouting matches as dogs bound up to toddlers, run between bike wheels, run too far from their owners. I hear the shouting every day from my balcony, so not wanting trouble, I keep close to the railings and keep my eyes on the Mersey.

And then I see it. A dolphin. The most unlikely thing I have ever seen in my life. A dolphin in the Mersey. Its black fin breaks the water only metres away. I shout, point, and everyone clusters around the railings.

Parents hoist their children up on their hips, they point, laugh, yell, 'A dolphin! look! a dolphin!' A small child calls, 'It's playing, Mummy,' and we all realise it is playing, it really is. We look at each other and our eyes shine with tears. A dolphin is playing. The miraculous is happening and we are all witness to it.

I stay as long as it does. I am thankful to see it heads back out to sea, not up to the Runcorn Industrial Estate where the fires still burn. I turn left into the park, still full of the golden glow of the miraculous.

But I have had enough luck for one day. There is no chance of being able to take my shoes off in this park. Rubbish overflows. Plastic containers are thrown into the pond, up trees, down the banks, abandoned in the middle of the grass.

This park was given money once; it was a sign of friendship with the East, a sister park. Large structures were built: a Chinese temple, a little lake, a Japanese garden, some big rock steps. But its glory days are long gone. There is nothing to be festive about now.

I sit by the pond for a bit, trying for some peace, or some wildlife, but all I see are midges hovering in the shade. The strange thing is there is no one here with me today, yet there is all this rubbish and under a birch tree, right by the path, there is a big burnt patch.

This puzzles me. I know England still burns its moorlands, instead of allowing re-wilding of forests, but this is a city park. 'It can't be slash and burn,' I think, 'why would someone garden like that these days?'

Laura tells me she meant barefoot inside the house, not at the park. She is horrified when I tell her I almost took my shoes off. 'Needles,' she says, 'best not to go.' I didn't think to look for needles, I just saw the obvious food packaging, not the truly dangerous stuff underneath.

Laura invites me out on Saturday night to The Baltic. She says, 'Don't judge us on our parks, come to the Cultural Hub, the centre of it all. You will see how friendly people are here.' It is close to our flats, we can walk, but we have to go slow, for my feet and for her shoes.

The Baltic is a cluster of warehouses turned into nightclubs. We have a drink in The Black Pearl and dance to the Beatles, because this is Liverpool and how can you not? The band are Beatles look-alikes, who play tambourines and guitars and flick their hair.

We all know all the words and stand on the concrete floor with one arm up in the air and the other holding a drink. We sing and drink and bounce and yell, 'She loves you yeah, yeah, yeah.' This public singing binds us close. We are the Beatles. We are Liverpool. We are one. 'Yeah. Yeah. Yeah.'

We stagger over the blocked-off streets to the Peaky Blinders Club. Laura pulls two caps out of her bag; she shoves one on my head and one on hers. Inside it is dark and full of men. They like it here, they like putting on a waistcoat and a peaked woollen cap and they like pretending to be gangsters.

They sit around old barrels, roll up their sleeves, and order whisky. The men are bold in here, they look for eye contact, they brush against arms, hands in pockets. Their costume gives them power and they know it.

Pete catches my eye at the bar. 'All right, love?' he asks. I nod and order a whisky. He hears my accent, smiles, holds out his hand. He says Kiwis are his favourite people, that he wants to go and live in New Zealand. Pete talks just like they do on *Coronation Street*, and it feels like I'm talking with a TV star.

He looks like he could be on television too, as he has the sort of face that would work on a screen. His cheekbones are high, his eyes dark under his peaked cap. He asks me over to his table, 'Meet my friends,' he says, 'we're friendly here, in Liverpool. We're not like England. We're like Ireland.'

His friends sit silently at the table, sleeves rolled up, arms folded. They give me a nod, then go back to watching the girls dancing.

There is a hens night happening in this club. The bride wears a white veil and has shoved a cap over the top. Her girlfriends have special T-shirts with 'Bridesmaid' printed on, in pink glitter. They egg the bride on, 'Last chance to be free!' they yell and push her into a man's lap. The girls all dance wildly, being free, taking all their last chances.

Pete tells me they are not locals, these girls. 'They fly in for their hen party weekends in towns where no one knows them so they can behave as badly as they want,' he says. 'They like taking last chances in a place where no one knows them.'

We talk of rituals, the loss of them and the reinvention of them. 'It's the mediaeval towns that get the most hen parties,' Pete yells at me over the music. 'It's as if the towns need ritual as well; they seem to call them in.'

Laura wants to move on, over the street to a new club, the Camp and Furnace. Pete comes with us and brings all his friends. There are rows of bench tables in long lines and we squeeze ourselves in the middle of the room.

It feels like I'm in the dining room of a boarding school. There are rows and rows of bench seats and no dance floor. Pete squishes in next to me and puts his arm around my waist. 'All right, love?' he yells.

The girl across from us clambers onto the long table, stands up and starts to dance. Then everyone does. Pete catches my hand and pulls me up on the table too. We jump on the desks, kick over seats, punch our arms in the air. I'm in the middle of a giant riot happening in the school dining room.

Pete hugs me close and yells in my ear, 'Will you marry me?'

Later, outside Pete tells me he isn't joking. He says, 'Being almost like Ireland isn't enough, I need to get out, I need another passport.' He's looking for a deal, a passport deal.

His friends are too. They nod, they say, 'If you don't want Pete, how about me?'

It takes a week to recover from the Baltic Cultural Centre.

It's been a long time since I danced on desks, since I drank too much and felt the rush, the power of a group. It unnerves me, this communal group power. It's too easy to get swept up in things, to become part of something I'm not part of at all.

So I lock myself in the flat.

My brother has a luscious green tree fern growing inside, a fern from home. I lie under that in the sun and listen to the lapping of the Mersey against the sea wall. It feels like I am in two places at once. When I lie down, I am home in New Zealand with my brother, the tree fern and the lapping river.

When I stand up and see properly, I am firmly in Liverpool with rubbish floating down the Mersey.

I don't know where I am or where I belong. It is a very strange feeling, one I know he lives with all the time. Maybe it's a feeling most of the world lives with, with so many displaced from homelands. It's tempting to make a miniature homeland inside the flat. It makes braving the other home, out on the street, easier.

The days get hotter, the news flashes 'Heatwave!'

I take a shuffle down to Festival Gardens. I think maybe this heatwave means people will be using the gardens again and they will be cleaned up. I am half right. People are using the gardens, but they haven't been cleaned up.

Dads in camouflage gear fish in the pond, while their children wade between the plastic bottles and chip packets to find tadpoles. Some families pitch a tent; they bring deck chairs and BBQs. They bring a lot of things down to the park and they walk away from most of it when they leave.

The boaties come out for the heatwave too. Big white yachts sail right by my flat, so close I can hear their talk, their laughter and I can see their bottles of champagne. I am startled. Can they not see the rubbish they are sailing in? There is a rusty shopping trolley over there, a floating rubbish bag just there. If they bent down they could hook it out, but they swoosh past. Full of good cheer.

Town is just one train stop away. I am almost in the city centre in this flat. I head to Liverpool One, the rebranded shopping centre. Here it is pedestrian only and we crowd the streets to get lots of new, cheap clothes.

Good fun is had all around, and not just by those shopping. There are public pianos, buskers, art installations and table tennis tables. Public free things that are just for fun. I think all the people who live in Liverpool must want to come into town every day. This is where it all happens.

Homelessness happens too. A lot of homelessness. The poor and destitute cluster around charity shops, bank machines and churches. They lean against the walls in their sleeping bags and hats, gathering their things close around them, their gloves, some cardboard, a paper cup. They make eye contact and call out, 'God bless you, love,' whether I give to them or not.

The people of Liverpool are kind, though, they bend down and speak, give a coffee, a sandwich, a wave. But it is cold out here on these streets at night, even in summer. There are so many empty buildings, and this is a rich country.

Hen parties stagger down the middle of the streets with their matching shirts and matching wine bottles. Some have sashes announcing their position, 'Mother of the Bride', or 'Maid of Honour'. They bunch up around the bride in her white veil. She wears a giant blow-up penis, sometimes strapped around her hips, sometimes around her neck. They parade through the streets, swinging wine bottles and shopping bags, laughing, yelling obscenities, looking for last chances.

I sit down on the edge of a concrete planter for a rest and to watch the brides and the buskers. It seems like there are still travelling players in this land. Today there are acrobats, fire dancers, singers, sword throwers and magicians.

The man next to me moves closer; he wants to talk. His name is Paul, he's a teacher and has been working in the Middle East. The band is good, it's very loud and I don't want to talk about work, but he pushes. He's out of a job. 'Passport problems,' he says. Then, 'Hey, why don't we get married? We could go anywhere on your passport.'

I laugh, tell him that's not going to happen and suddenly I have a fight on my hands.

Paul stands up and shouts at me, 'What's wrong with me? Hey? What's wrong with me? I would be a good husband. I would let you go out.'

People start gathering around, keen for a fight, they pull their phones out to record. I get up and slip through the crowd to leave.

I hear him still yelling at me, 'You're too picky! You won't give me a chance! I would be a good husband!'

The homeless call to me, 'God bless you, love.' Buskers sing into their microphones. Table tennis balls fly. Boys wanting to be girls are dressed up as boys. Evangelists call out to the wretched. Seagulls screech. Knife throwers take off their shirts. And all is tumultuous.

I am more and more grateful for my brother's flat. It's nice here, lying under the tree fern in dappled green light.

I look over to the Wirral from my balcony. It has a sort of mythic thing going on. People acknowledge that Liverpool can be pretty grim, 'but over on the Wirral ...' becomes the catch phrase. I can see green patches over there, in between the heavy industry, the cranes, the round concrete containers.

Beyond the Wirral the mountains of Wales rise, a smudge of purple. These are my consolation. For I know the magic still bubbles up in Wales. How can it not? King Arthur sleeps down there, in Caerleon. I know he is just in a long, long sleep, and when he is needed, he will rise again with his knights and Excalibur and everything will be alright.

In the morning I cup my hands and call from my balcony across the Mersey and into Wales. 'King Arthur! It's time. The people, the river, the land needs you. Wake up. We need you, King Arthur! Bring Merlin too, if you can.'

Pete asks me out on a day trip to Port Sunlight even though I won't marry him. He tells me it's the Jewel of the Wirral and I must go. He says it is on all the lists of the best things to see in England. Pete tells me he likes lists.

So on Sunday we catch the train out together and he is right. It is a jewel, especially in the middle of a hot summer. There is no dog poo in Port Sunlight, there is no rubbish on the ground, or people in their pyjamas.

Instead, people play bowls on the village green. A choir practises in the community centre and a knitting club sits out under the lime trees. Little girls run by with bows in their hair. There are roses in the public gardens and fountains and art.

The houses have small lead-glass windows and quaint turrets made from hand-hewn stone. They are named too. We walk past 'The Squirrels', 'Greystone', 'The Larks'.

Wisteria winds around the name plates, poppies sway at the front doors.

There is a summer garden competition, and we are all allowed to vote. Pete links his arm with mine and we stroll through avenues of trees. We peer into people's gardens and rank them according to the criteria. Pete is in his element; 'I love ranking things,' he says, 'it's good to have winners, and I like deciding who is the best. I think I would make a good judge.'

He gives marks for tidiness and wants to show me his scores. I give marks for wildness and keep my scores hidden.

There are a lot of people out walking, paper and pen in hand, rating the gardens just like us. But we are all quiet. It is so quiet it feels like people must use hand signals, flags or high-pitched whistles to communicate. 'Do they still use semaphore here?' I whisper to Pete, but he just shakes his head and goes, 'Shush, it's impolite to be loud.'

There are three games of bowls happening on the small village green, at least a hundred women are playing and more watch from the seats under the trees, but it is completely quiet. Hands rise and fall, heads shake or are raised sharply, and I think I see a flag in one woman's pocket.

It feels like there is something else going on in this town, something secret. Houses have candles in their attic windows, with black curtains hanging at the sides. 'Could be signalling in the night,' I whisper. 'Smuggling, you know, war stuff, adventure stuff.'

Pete sighs, 'They are just nostalgic here, Sarah,' he says. 'They like hanging onto our glorious past.'

I think of the chaos in the city and I don't blame them. I would like a little house here and I would definitely put a candle in the attic. If glorious pasts were a thing, I would like one of those too.

We sit outside a tea shop under bulky chestnut trees, their leaves crunchy on the dry grass. We have tea and cakes, and all is still and peaceful. I even hear a bird, a songbird. I am so startled; it seems such an unusual thing to hear that I stand up. 'A bird! A bird!' I gasp, clutching Pete's shoulder and peering up into the tree. 'I know I heard a bird up there!'

Pete says, "Port Sunlight is the sort of place you will hear a bird in. I heard it too.'

I keep a close eye out now I know there are real jewels to be found here and I see more: a white butterfly, two low-flying bumblebees.

There is an art gallery in this village, a wonderful gallery full of famous art, and it is free. I am struck by the art here for I see things in these paintings I hadn't seen before. What I notice now is how different the landscapes look from real life. They have variety, they have clean rivers, there is no rubbish. These landscapes look unreal now, from a different world where rivers really did run clean, where birds really did live in trees. It all seems extraordinary. Unbelievable. Works of Fantasy.

We catch the train home. It is mostly a ride in the dark for the train runs under the Mersey itself. It does seem strange that something like Port Sunlight can exist so close to my suburb, and just a quick underwater trip brings you out there.

Back in my flat I feel the pull of Port Sunlight, the pull of nostalgia and innocence. I understand now why people look wistfully out to the Wirral, out to Wales, and smile a little at the mention of those names. Underneath the modern city, Liverpool does feel nostalgic too. Vintage clothing is cool. Musicals are booked out. Theatre that looks to the past is wildly popular. The Beatles rule.

Any era is cool and celebrated except for the one right now. People are scared of the one right now, this Brexit era. People appear friendly and easy going, but underneath they are worried. There is hushed talk of stockpiling food and medicine, about being unable to leave, of planes grounded, of backlogs, of visas being needed to go to football games in Europe, of a brain drain, of no more cheap holidays in Spain. Of no more cheap anything.

Laura tells me she is trying to grow food inside her flat. She is worried about food shortages and riots. I ask her about allotments. People dug for victory in the war, and I'm sure they can do it again. She says, 'Allotments outside are too risky; anything outside is too risky.'

She whispers of riots and lockdowns. She tells me she wants to grow potatoes inside, up against the window and pumpkins. She asks, 'How much light do blackcurrants need?' She's reading up on inside gardening and is ready to do what's needed. 'I will fertilise everything with my paintbrush!' she declares.

What she really wants is a bolt hole, somewhere peaceful and somewhere with a valuable passport. I tell Laura about Pete and his marriage proposal. She says, 'We all want to be Irish; we think we are anyway, with Liverpool being so close. We all want an Irish granny and her passport, and if we don't have one, a Kiwi is the next best thing.'

Secretly, I count my blessings, for I am a Kiwi and I have an Irish granny. I am overwhelmed with good fortune.

Pete rings again; he wants to take me out to Blackpool for the day, even though I tell him there is absolutely no chance of marriage. He tells me it's fun, hanging out with me, listening to my accent, and he likes my jokes. I always have a soft spot for someone who likes my jokes and I like the seaside so I say yes.

He picks me up in his tiny car early and drives us up through incomprehensible motorways where roads make giant circles around themselves and everything looks the same.

We park in the backstreets, outside little boarding houses with fake grass lawns. There are signs advertising holiday accommodation. Pete tells me he comes here on holiday sometimes. 'It's a lovely break,' he says, 'here at the seaside.'

I am astonished. I don't know what kind of holiday it would be with all this fake grass, with narrow little boarding houses and the wind tunnelling through them.

We walk down to the beach where the Ferris wheels and tattoo parlours are. It's hard to see the beach because the high concrete sea wall blocks any view. It doesn't matter, though, as people only have eyes for the rides, the candy and the bright lights. There is a big black tower, way off in the distance. I point to that and say, 'Let's go there.'

We stop for fish and chips for lunch first. 'Traditional fare,' both Pete and the signs tell me. This county, Lancashire, is the birthplace of fish and chips. The first shop was opened around 1863 just down the road. I choose the most traditional eatery I can find and we sit down to this ancient feast. I slip my shoes off, curl my toes into the plastic grass, and eat my pile of soggy chips.

We watch people walk the strip while we eat. It seems

everyone wants to be a princess here, and indeed you can be. Men and women wear shiny ball dresses, tiaras and glitter. Neon, velvet and wings work for everyone. Plumed white horses pull fairy tale Cinderella coaches in between the slow pulsing cars.

Everyone is dressed up and ready. They want their Mr Right. I look over at Pete, eating soggy chips, and wonder if I tried a little harder, if I saw him in a different light, whether he could turn into Mr Right. I wonder if it's just me, if I really am getting way too picky and should just settle for someone keen. Pete certainly is keen.

But I am starting to question whether Mr Right would make anything right at all.

I go inside to use the bathroom. There is an old couple sitting inside at the window and I don't know if they are real or not. They are completely still, tea cups poised, small smiles on their faces. I almost can't fit up the stairs; they seem to be made for dolls only.

It's hard negotiating my body in the bathroom, as there is nowhere to turn and even my breathing seems to push against the flimsy walls. I have to back down the stairs and turn at the bottom. Definitely a holiday in one of these places would be impossible. I would have to back everywhere and only turn outside, like a car.

Downstairs the couple are still there, at the window, cups raised, smiling sweetly. I really don't know if they are a permanent thing. If they are Art.

It's a long walk to the black tower. After half an hour it still looks far away so we settle for the central pier instead. We kick through the paper cups, food wrappings and plastic bags at our feet and line up in the long queue for the Ferris wheel.

When we are high up, we look down onto the empty beach. I ask Pete why no one is at the beach, even though we have this heatwave. He says, 'Everyone is at the beach, this is the beach, this is what we do, we go for rides, go shopping and go to shows.'

He is right, that is what we are all doing. Advertising posters plaster the posts, we could see *Cinderella*, or *Teletubbies Live* tonight if we wanted.

There is a fortune teller on the pier too, with red velvet curtains over her little alcove. Pete and I slow down when we pass her, along with everyone else. We all want to go in, to know. But also we don't. Her sign says her lineage is Ancient Romany. A true gypsy.

A woman in front of us pushes the curtain aside and slips in. I get a flash of a crystal, a golden altar before the curtain falls back. We all linger, wanting to see her when she comes out, whether she hurries away, tight lipped, head down. If she cries.

Pete tells me he has been to one of these fortune tellers. 'She told me I was going to live over the sea,' he says and squeezes my hand.

'Probably Spain then,' I reply. 'Lots of Brits in Spain, soaking up that sun in their old age. You would love it there.'

We are lucky in Blackpool today: there is a dog show on. Pete tells me, 'This is a big cultural thing. We love our dogs and we love our dog shows,' so we stop to watch. Pete is in his element again. 'I bet I can pick the winner,' he says. 'I'm good at picking winners; I know what to look for.'

We watch the competition for 'The Prettiest Girlie'.

There are bows, ribbons and curled hair on both the dogs and their owners. There are jumps and ramps in a big ring, but the Prettiest Girlie doesn't have to do any dazzling tricks. She just has to stand there wearing ribbons in her fur.

There seems to be no criteria either, with different breeds, sizes and ages all in together. The owners introduce their dogs and justify their inclusion. 'She is a rescued dog', or 'She only has one leg' or 'The gypsies threw her over the fence.'

I ask Pete what the criteria for judging is. He looks at me curiously, 'Just the prettiest,' he says. He points to the smallest dog. 'I bet she wins.'

The judges walk up and down the lineup. They announce that 'The Prettiest Girlie' is won by Chloe, the smallest, most delicate dog in the competition. I wonder about that, the size and the female thing and what that is really saying.

Pete squeezes my hand. 'Right again,' he says.

We escape the crowds and go down to the beach, 'Pleasure Beach' it is called, and it really is a pleasure. The sand is golden, the water silver. We roll up our pants and paddle in the Irish Sea. We walk back to the car down the beach, scuffing through the shallows. Pete puts his arm around my shoulder, and it feels good.

Not good enough for marriage, though. Especially not good enough for a passport marriage. He drops me home, gives me a hug, and tells me he wants to take me to the flower show at Southport tomorrow. 'It's a great cultural experience, Sarah, even more than a dog show. We Brits love our gardens.'

I like gardens too, and I like cultural experiences so it appears I have another date with Pete.

We catch the train to the show, along with all the old people in the entire world. We line up in the queue at Southport to get in and I realise this is the perfect place for me. Everyone walks slower than me; there are plenty of stick walkers and shufflers and I fit in. It's okay to clutch the railings and just breathe for a bit and no one minds how slow the queue moves.

The queue continues inside, snaking around the stalls selling gumboots, patio plants and garden gnomes. Pete steers me towards the show gardens, the ones in the competition for Gold Trophies. The queue becomes a standstill here. Around me I hear mutterings, 'Too much work,' and, 'Oh, it's lovely, but it's too big for me.'

Pete pushes through and gets us voting forms for the 'People's Choice' awards. He gets out two pens from his shirt pocket, one for me and one for him. He mutters at me, telling me what to vote for, insisting I tick the same boxes as him.

'I can make my own decisions,' I say, irritated.

Pete looks up and replies, 'It's just that you're not from here, and you're voting in our show and I don't think you understand that privilege.'

He bends over his form, ticking his boxes. I give him his pen back, and I shuffle quietly away from him in the slow-moving river of old people. I am pleased that I insisted on keeping my own train ticket for the return home in my own pocket. I'm pleased that I have my own passport and that I have kept it safe, on its own. I am pleased I never have to see Pete in my life again.

I find a plastic chair in the middle of the field and listen to the entertainment. The community choir sings 'What a Wonderful World' and the audience sings along. They have brought sandwiches, flasks of tea and woollen knee rugs and have settled themselves in for a day's singsong. Chairs are pulled close together, people bunch up and sing loudly to everything. They clap. They lift their faces to the sun.

An announcement comes over the loudspeaker. 'Ted is lost. He is wearing a green jumper, he is 6 foot tall, aged 82. He may, or may not, know his name.'

I think my neighbour could be Ted. He is sitting alone, he has a green jumper on, he looks at least 82. But he is singing at the top of his voice, he has both hands swaying in the air and is having a lovely time. I think about suggesting the lost tent to him, but I can't bear to stop his fun.

I look around to see if I should ask someone, but I see most of my neighbours look like they too could be Ted. All of them are having a wonderful time. I keep quiet. I don't suggest anything.

I shuffle back into the queue to see the rest of the stalls. There are food stalls, clothing stalls, but by far the most popular is the one giving away free samples of gin. The queue stops here. People push through to the front and they stay. I think I see Ted in there too, and he's having a marvellous time. He has a free sample in each hand and is laughing loudly.

I pass the lawnmower stall. Mostly they have shifted everything from the lawnmower museum in town out here to the stall. There is nothing to buy in here, only things to marvel over, to reminisce about. There are blades and scythes and motors and in here and the smell of grass is especially potent. There are an awful lot of green-jumpered men in this tent. All aged 82. All who may or may not know their name.

On the way home I stop at Crosby Beach, home to the most remarkable art. Down on the sand is a cast-iron man standing looking out to sea. The man is reproduced 100 times for two miles up the beach. Some men are more out to sea than others. Some are up to their necks in water.

Someone has dressed the one closest to the shore. He has an old green jumper on. Maybe Ted got here before me. This statue stands in the brown swash, and it looks as if he is walking straight into the sea. What he walks towards is even more startling.

Giant wind turbines and cargo ships are out there in the channel, art installations in their own right. It is strangely, deeply moving, this art. It talks of our solitude, of our unease, of our future. People are quiet around this art.

There are also prehistoric footprints along this coast, which go all the way up past Formby. I hunt for them at the edge of the sea on the old mud layers. The signs tell me there are female footprints, 'UK shoe size 1 to 7'. Being a UK shoe size 7 myself I hunt for prints that could be my double 7000 years ago.

I hunt for a woman who lived out in the wilds when there truly were wilds. Who lived with boars, wolves and aurochs, for their footprints are here too. I think of her, walking these beaches just like me, keeping an eye out for her kids, just like I would.

There are preserved prints of her children too, and their prints run round and round in circles. It makes me extraordinarily happy to think of prehistoric kids running in circles and playing on the sand.

On the weekend I put my pack on and walk down to Lark Lane farmers market. I figure the more I can avoid the supermarket the better. Lark Lane is the hip place in town. It's crammed with cool cafés serving coffee and smashed avocado on toast. In the old post office there are classes on yoga, veganism and chanting.

The footpath has been patched up recently and I see a child's footprint in it; they couldn't resist the wet concrete. I smile. I bet its prehistoric ancestor wouldn't have resisted that either. Maybe in another 7000 years it will be roped off and people will gasp. 'Shoe size 2,' the sign will say, 'Running in circles around the pub.'

I'm excited about the market, though. I bring my pack to put all my fresh produce in, but when I get there I realise there may not be many farmers around these parts. There are hardly any stalls. Mostly this market sells pork pies and cake. I buy some cake. I sign a petition to keep the library open, and another one to stop health cuts. The woman with the petitions tells me she loves living in Liverpool. 'It's a special place here,' she says. 'It's like Ireland, only cleaner.'

I am getting worried about these references to Ireland. I plan to go there next. It is the home of my father and, by extension, me. I don't know if I want to go if it is dirtier and less friendly than Liverpool.

I look down at the broken glass squashed into the mud. I say to the petition woman, 'It isn't that clean here. Look at this glass.'

She peers down, 'That's nothing, you should see Ireland,' she says. 'We are much cleaner. And friendlier.'

Lark Lane leads into Sefton Park which is where I meet

Laura for a walk. Everyone loves this park, and rightly so, for it has ancient trees, ponds, fields, grottos and a glasshouse.

I am a bit early so I sit in the glasshouse on a marble seat and marvel at the glory. Bougainvillea climbs the sides and hangs off the ceiling, all pink and orange. Yellow datura flowers umbrella, and banana palms push their leaves up to the roof. I am in fairy land.

There is a wedding here tonight and the staff are getting ready. When Laura turns up, she tells me how much she would love a wedding here. 'Or anywhere really,' she sighs, 'as long as it's a beautiful fairy tale wedding.'

A wrought-iron staircase spirals up to the balcony which runs around the top. Balls of white gypsophila are carried in and buckets of pink lilies. It is gaspingly beautiful. It's easy to believe in happily ever after, here in this bubble of enchantment. It's easy to believe in romance, in Prince Charming, in Mr Right.

It's not so easy outside.

We kick through plastic bags, along the pond and down to the grotto. These are railed off nowadays and look like prison cells with big bars at their entrance. They are filled with rubbish. Maybe it's a game, to see how far you can throw your drink bottle into the cave.

I think of how special designers were brought in from overseas to make these, the money it took, the creativity. These grottos were the height of garden fashion, and now they are a rubbish bin.

I ask Laura about the lack of wildlife here. I say, 'It seems like *Silent Spring*. I haven't seen a spider in my flat, or fly, or a single bee, and this is midsummer.'

She sighs and says, 'We still have wildlife, Sarah. We still have rats.'

On my way out of the park I look at the information signs at the park entrance. One says 'Please don't feed the rats'. Laura is right. We still have rats.

I walk home through the rubbish dump of Festival Gardens and now there are four large burnt patches. Some of the wooden seats are charred as well. I know this is not gardening. I know this is arson.

I come home, back to my red brick square flat, and I realise this place is getting me down. There is just so much rubbish and despair that I can feel myself sinking. I feel for the passport hunters, for the homeless, for the brides with their hope of happily ever after. I feel for all the despondent secret eaters in my neighbourhood and for those who want to burn things. But mostly I feel for the death of the wild.

I just don't know how people manage here without their own private manor house to retreat to. I figure the only thing to do is to pretend.

I start with the Mersey. I pretend that it's really clean, that the brown sludge is really golden sand, that the indentations in it are more prehistoric footprints. That forest comes right down to its banks and the things floating are just branches from the storms. When the sun is really low in the sky, I can see that the water is silver, sometimes even blue.

I pretend the people who swoosh by in their huge yachts on the weekends are my best friends and I wave to them. They wave back and laugh and raise their glasses to me and I realise that they too are playing a game.

I pretend that The Festival Gardens are my own private

estate. I go down and pick up all the rubbish in my favourite part, at the back by the hazel trees, and that becomes my own garden. I pretend that the four burnt patches are not caused by arsonists but are bare ground, tilled and ready for planting. Daffodils maybe.

I pretend that the woodland walks really are diverse and there are badgers, deer, wild boar and lynx deep in the woods. I pretend that the plastic bottles floating in the pond are really waterlilies. I bring my picnic blanket and lie down with my book with the other families, and we wave and smile at the children.

I name the flat 'The Lighthouse' and pretend it actually is one. I put a lantern upstairs out behind the railing and I light it at night. I pretend that the apartment block is not square red brick, but white and round and shines out.

I now live in a splendid beacon of safety.

I rearrange all the furniture. I hang up blue and white flags. I pretend the tree fern is a specimen from exotic travels. I use my hands as binoculars. I run to the balcony and salute the navy ships and the police boats when they motor past.

I pretend I see dolphins in the river every morning, and I call out to them.

I pretend that Port Sunlight is really the name for the whole of Liverpool, and we all are living in pools of sunlight and roses and birds.

I pretend the passport hunters, Pete and his friends, are knights looking for a quest of sacred love into foreign lands.

Then I think that this is the really powerful thing about England: its ability to pretend. This is what all the great writers have done. Stories of magic and fantasy come from this land: Harry Potter, Narnia, Lord of the Rings, Winnie the Pooh, Peter Pan.

If we just all pretend, we can truly believe that we are magical, that there are elves and wizards and Hundred Acre Woods. And we can pretend we are the good guys, that colonialism was a great sharing of culture, a gift to the world. We can pretend we always win the wars because we have Tinkerbell, Churchill, Gandalf, Robin Hood, Dumbledore, Aslan, the Queen and Pooh Bear on our side.

We can pretend that this slow, green land is a wonderful place for all. We can pretend in a glorious past. We can go on pretending this forever.

I hang on to the belief that King Arthur is coming. Surely that is not pretence.

# TEN

# The Road Rises

## IRELAND

I HAVE BEEN THINKING OF WHAT KOSTAS TOLD ME
that night of my birthday dinner. 'Find the techniques of
your ancestors,' he said. 'Find out how they connected into
their land, learn the ancient ways of your people. It will
show you the way home.'

I have felt the pull of Ireland all my life, but I've also felt
wary. Dad has warned me off this land. 'Don't go back,
Sarah, don't pick at the old wounds,' he would tell me.

There are terrible wounds in Ireland, big enough to
force my father and his siblings to flee. So I have been
putting it off and putting it off. What if Dad is right? What
if it really is terrible? What then? But what if it is glorious?
What if it tears me in half? What then?

I am also broke so I need some sort of job. Late at night I
look on the Woofing Ireland website and enter myself as a
willing worker. In the morning I have four offers of farm
placements. I know I need to go south, away from the border
town and the troubles my father fled. I choose a place on the

east coast, close to the main bus route to Dublin. Just in case it's terrible. Just in case I have to do a runner in the night.

I wear my farm boots and my old woollen jumper on the plane. It feels good to arrive in Ireland dressed down, as inconspicuous as possible. I have this strange feeling that the land itself may recognise me, rise up and create all sorts of chaos.

There is a bus down the coast, so I get that, and Jenny meets me at the pub in town. We recognise each other by our boots and jumpers. Hers have more mud, though. I think Jenny has been out in the wind for her whole life. Even though the evening is still, she is more windswept than anything I have met before.

And her car seems to be rewilding itself. The floor has twigs, earth, seeds. I think some could be sprouting so I'm careful where I put my feet. On the drive home she tells me of her family, her husband Niall who is a consultant, her grown children Ted, Grace, Liam, and her three grandchildren. The trees press in on both sides of the car and she races us home through golden green tunnels.

The farmhouse is hidden behind high hedges, and it is full of people and dogs. We go into the kitchen and I am given a cup of tea and set to cutting up carrots. I have arrived in the middle of a family reunion.

Liam is home from America and everyone has come to see him and his new wife and baby. They sit around the kitchen table, slicing potatoes. They talk about America as if it's another province of Ireland, just over there, full of all the people they love.

I feel awkward. My accent is all wrong, I don't know the

ways people speak here or the ways things are done. But Niall leans over and says, 'Sure Ireland doesn't have any tourists. Your accent is all strange, but your heart isn't. You are just one of us returning home.'

It seems I am very lucky. Maybe I have the luck of the Irish after all. There are good people sitting around this table. I may not need to do that runner.

In the morning, my job is to make hay.

I try to hide my incredulous look. Hay making? In this day and age? But what about the twentieth century? I want to ask. Instead, I duck my head, pick up a pitchfork and clump off to the upper edge of the field.

'Just toss it into a pile,' Niall yells after me.

My hands blister up in the first 20 seconds. The insides of my thumbs become raw, but I keep tossing bits of hay. I have no technique. I think of my grandmother, tossing hay, of my great-grandmother, and I try a little harder. It doesn't make it any better. It is nice, though, when I get to take a break and lie down in the hay in this little field that slopes towards the sun. I feel good then.

Almost Irish.

There are a lot of people here. Jenny and Niall preside over a large family and a large community. Everyone is welcome, even random people like me. If you will sit down in the kitchen and have a cup of tea you belong here.

The rooms in the house are full so Grace and her boyfriend Finn have moved into a big bell tent in the garden for the summer. They have the nicest place of all out there under the apple trees. Grace asks me out to the tent for a drink in the evening. She shows me the honey mead she is brewing in white plastic buckets. We sit on the grass and toast to my first day of work.

It's good to toast with honey mead, the heroes drink. And I do feel heroic here, having slayed the nervousness of the diasporic return, having made the choice to not keep turning my back on this ancestral past.

We toast to me, and to Queen Maeve. 'The Queen of Fairies,' Grace says with a little wink. Grace pours a little mead out for her too, on the earth between us. 'Got to keep the Queen happy,' she grins at me. 'Here's to all our Queendoms!'

For the next week I work with Jenny, Grace and Finn in the garden. Jenny talks about permaculture; she teaches it in the evenings down at the community centre, and she looks at me as another student. It's nice, being a student here and not a teacher. Jenny spends days showing me how to garden like a forest does, in layers, and interdependent.

I don't see Niall much, who is busy consulting I am told. He has an office in the house somewhere, but I never find it. He appears in doorways a lot and announces he's off to the post office. He always asks me if I want to go too, but I don't get any post here. I haven't sent or received proper letters in the post for quite a few years now.

I am here in autumn, the harvest season. One of the things I most like about gardening is picking things, so this is the best season for me. I am given a big basket and sent off to pick hazelnuts with Finn.

Finn climbs the tree, leans on the branches and gives them a good shake. The nuts fall from the sky like a lolly scramble. They are round and fat and have a green papery covering. They look like tiny presents, all wrapped up in their own loveliness.

Once we have walked around the tree one way picking up the nuts we turn, walk the other way and gather just as many again. 'Change the way you look at things and you always discover more,' Finn says. 'It's all about perspective. Trees teach us everything.'

I stand with my back against the tree trunk and look out and see as the tree sees, through a haze of golden green. I think I have a lot to learn here, from these trees and these people.

It is also mushroom season. Finn is very interested in mushrooms. He goes on mushroom identification courses and has all sorts of books on them. We walk up the road and into the glen to forage, our baskets swinging, our dog sniffing around the banks.

A flash car stops, two men get out. They are Dubliners down for an early-morning forage in the forest. They have seen our basket and recognise fellow foragers. They open their car boot and show us their mushroom hoard. We pick them up and they get passed around for a sniff and a nibble.

'Foraging is the best thing to make a man well,' says one. They are gleeful, they rub their hands together, they talk of luck. They get back in the car and yell out the window, 'Off home for a grand breakfast!'

Finn and I strike off the road and go deep into the old forest. Tall chestnuts and oaks tower above us while we crunch through their orange leaves. There are still wild blueberries, purple and dusky. I eat them, the last of summer, while Finn tells me where to look for mushrooms.

He says they like mossy banks. So do I for they are dappled with fallen leaves and magic.

It's hard to tell if something is a mushroom, a pool of sunlight or a small pot of gold. Things shift here in the blink of an eye.

'The mushrooms want us to find them,' says Finn, 'but they don't make it easy.'

Sometimes we find one guarding a hole in a tree. The hole looks like it leads deep underground. We don't take those ones. It seems asking for trouble to take those ones.

The dog disappears. She has her own business in these woods, Finn tells me.

When we have enough for our own grand breakfast we crunch through the leaves back home. We gather round the range, mushrooms sizzling in the pan. We rub our hands gleefully and talk of luck.

I get the weekends off. I hadn't realised that was part of the deal and I don't really know what to do. Seeing I'm in the gardening business now I decide to go to Mount Usher Gardens for a walk around.

Niall gives me a lift on his way to the post office. We stop for coffee and cake in the garden's café. Niall seems to know the cake choices in this cabinet remarkably well. He orders both of us huge slices of chocolate cake with extra cream.

'Now, don't tell the others,' he says. 'Sure I do appreciate the organic healthy food at home. But this cake,' he sighs, 'and so handy with the post office just there. Now to tell you the truth I don't get any letters at all; I haven't for quite a few years now. I just come here and eat cake instead.'

When I buy my ticket for the gardens the lady says,

'Now prepare yourself, this is not just a walk in the gardens you know, this is a practice walk for heaven.'

She is right. There is a slow river, tall trees, soft light and abundant beauty piles up upon itself. I spend most of the afternoon in the wildflower meadow with the butterflies and the low golden sun. I lie back and breathe in the dry earth and the end of summer.

In my stillness small insects land on me. My hair becomes full of seeds. Nearby a father kneels in the wildflowers in front of his baby. He twirls an orange leaf in his fingers; she laughs and reaches out. Tiny brown butterflies twist around each other in their own tornado of love. A bright red dragonfly lands on my arm.

There is a stone house in the middle of these gardens, and people still live there. It is on the other side of the river. I wonder how it must feel to wake up on a warm autumn morning, to have breakfast on the lawn and wonder whether to ride your pony or read your book. The force field of the river keeps the tourists out of bounds but, still, you must feel them watching, marvelling, wishing they could be you for a bit, or forever.

Back home I sort seeds with Jenny. She has been collecting them in brown paper bags. We shake the seed heads, pull them apart and pour them into envelopes. We store them in an old biscuit tin for next year. 'Sure, you have to save your seeds, Sarah,' she says, 'keep them safe and don't forget about them. Grow them in the spring. Keep them living and save their lives.'

It feels good to sit in the kitchen with a friend, drinking tea and sorting seeds. There are mushrooms drying over the range, pumpkins piled up in the sunny corner to harden. Basil and garlic hang from the wooden beams.

I talk about Billy and Ellowyn and show her pictures. Jenny says, 'Sure they must miss you, and your land must too.'

I hadn't thought of that. My land, missing me.

I am quiet for a while. Jenny goes on, 'The land here misses people too, all those millions of people we lost through emigration and starvation. We went from 12 million to 4 million. The land feels that loss and the land grieves. It still remembers what it was. Can you feel it? It even grieves for you, her own daughter with her heart planted in another land now. Try to listen, to feel what the land feels, what it remembers.'

Jenny tells me to talk to everything, to listen to everything. We label the seeds carefully, using their proper scientific names. 'Use the plants' names when you speak to them and you will really come to know them,' she says. 'They will become your friends.'

I try hard. Many of the things supposed to be my friends are things I would cut down at home. I reason the gorse and broom can be my temporary friends, and as soon as I get home I will unfriend them.

Sometimes I come across pots with unscientific labels. One is called, 'Very Tasty', another 'The thing from just over there'.

With so many people to feed there is much potato peeling to be done. This family loves potatoes. Grace says, 'I have tried pasta and rice, but it feels like I'm eating air; there is nothing of substance. Not like a good potato. I could eat those forever.'

Grace is very pretty. She has long curling hair and even in her farmer's clothes she is ravishing. By the light of the fire in the evenings she turns into a goddess. She has a part-time job in a pub in Dublin on Saturday nights and I think her weekends are a lot wilder than her weeks. I think she is content with reading gardening books and brewing honey mead during the week because she is recovering from those weekends.

She gives me a lift to Dublin on my next weekend off. I walk the streets and think of my father. He told me stories of coming down to Dublin and eating jelly in the cafés. It was the highlight of his childhood. I try to find that highlight too, but there is no jelly to be had in the cafés of Dublin nowadays. Still, it's fun walking around on streets I have heard of all my life and fun to imagine how it would feel to have been brought up here, to really belong.

I go to the National Museum when it starts to rain. It's warm and it's free. I wander around, astonished at what is in here. A dragon would be proud of this hoard of gold. I stop at signs announcing, 'Two gold torcs' and 'Nine gold beads'. This gold shines out of its case, begging to be around the neck of a beauty like Grace.

Hoards of gold have been found sunken in lakes and bogs, in the most unlikely places. This gold was never meant to be found. But here it is shining out, linking us to the ancient ones who wore it. We all stare, dumbfounded, and shuffle around the cases.

The bog bodies draw a crowd too. They are 5000-year-old bodies preserved by the peat bogs. Their skin shrunken over bones, their fingernails still intact. We alive ones shake our heads and draw in our breath. There are mutterings of Druids, magic and ancient things.

On the way home I talk of all that gold and how maybe in the garden if we dug down, we too could find a hoard. Grace says, 'Firstly we have a no-dig garden, and secondly why would you be interested in other people's gold?'

It has been a long hot summer and the harvest is abundant. I am astonished at the amount of food this small farm produces. I see what I could do with my own place at home. The climate is just like this and I could grow all of this too. I watch very carefully, I learn about training loganberries, making elderberry tonic, cider vinegar, and rosehip oil. I learn about forest gardens, permaculture, and the building of resilience.

In the evenings I drink honey mead with Grace and Queen Maeve.

When most of the picking is done our energy becomes focused on building the earth. We spread compost over the garden beds, we water even though there are no plants in the ground. The worms still need water, don't forget them, I am told.

We spend a lot of time looking and planning as well. It's good to take a cup of tea and sit in the field and talk of turning it all into a forest garden. Or a giant hedge.

'It's a fine thing to have a field facing the sun and a good hedge,' Jenny tells me. Walking the hedges is just as important as working in the garden. 'It's important to walk around and admire these trees,' she says, laying her hand on the trunks of spreading oaks, hawthorns, golden ashes. 'They need to feel your hands, your footfall, hear your voice, in order to know they are loved. No use just saying it from the kitchen table.'

Jenny shows me where the ladybirds are nesting. We bend down, part leaves and there they are: shiny, round and quiet in the afternoon sun. 'Whatever you do, don't disturb this place,' she whispers. 'We need these ladybirds.'

There are lots of rustling noises in the hedge. I ask Jenny if there are birds or hedgehogs nesting there. She nods, looking at me sideways, and says, 'Sure those rustlings aren't any of our business.'

'You let what rustles in a hedge well alone.'

In the old church down the lane there is a concert for Irish Heritage week. We all go. The boys comb their hair and put on their tweed jackets. Grace comes down the stairs in her new red dress and pulls everyone's eyes.

Ted says, 'Ah would you look at our Grace, looking like a fairy in her new wool dress.'

And, indeed, she does. Her dress matches the red berries gleaming in the dark yew trees in the churchyard entrance. It feels like I'm walking inside a Christmas card.

We sit in boxed wooden pews, crammed up for the church is full. The musicians are local lads on their pipes and whistles. They play jigs and reels, traditional music it's billed as but it seems as popular as any modern music. They play 'King of the Fairies'. It's music I want to laugh and twirl to, and it's music I want to sob to. It feels like music I would follow anywhere, even if it led me down the holes in those trees.

I lean over and whisper, 'Grace, this is real, isn't it? It's real music from real fairies.'

She shakes her head and whispers back, 'Ah sure there's

not fairies out there. Just be careful of their music. Sometimes, if you have the right ears for it, you can catch one of their songs from the wind. That's what they say.'

There is no percussionist in the band, but I hear a lot of drumming. In the pew in front of me I see children's heads bobbing up and down. I realise their little feet are dancing away unseen down below, marking time, filling in the gaps in the music. Then I realise most of the adults have their feet going as well; they remain sitting, but their feet are drumming time. I look down and across and I see dancing feet everywhere.

Some children break out and dance in the aisle, their hands by their sides, their little cheeks bright red, their feet going wild. These children are giving their whole beings to the dance, and their eyes gleam as they feel the rush of joy. And I feel it too, just sitting here. I also feel busts of euphoria in these spinning reels.

I think back to those singing rocks on the Camino. The singing from deep earth places in Guinea and the way those drums opened up my ears. I remember Amadou saying, 'To listen properly is one of the biggest joys in a life. Listening can burst open a heart.' Looking at all of this, listening to this, I know he is right.

They play 'Port Na bPúcaí', a song from the Blasket Islands. A song that tells of fishermen who went out to sea for the day and came home wild eyed, windswept and all singing the same song. It was one they heard trembling through their sealskin boat. It is the song the whales sang out there that day. The music passed through sealskin and human skin and bound them all.

It is strange being here, where myth is real. Where whales

sing and here is their music, where fairies dance and here is their gold. Where Queen Maeve is poured a drink and it is swallowed.

When we get home Ted goes straight to bed. He says he has to get up very early the next morning. He is very interested in the old forest and is making a documentary about the moss there. He wants to hide his recording device in the moss, high above the cliff walk.

'I want to hear what the moss has to say when I'm not there,' he says, 'so I have to sneak up early to hide my recorder so the moss doesn't see me.'

Now I know the place, I am trusted on my own to do things. I am starting to become useful I am told. I get a basket for sweet chestnuts, find the dog's lead and call out that I'm going up to the forest. Jenny tells me to come home if the mist comes up.

'I don't mind getting damp,' I say, 'it's only mist.'

Jenny gives me a hard look. 'Sure the good people might not like it,' she says.

And I realise we are talking about fairies. I stop and look her straight in the eye. 'So you're telling me fairies are real then?'

She shoots a glance out the window, 'Ah that's just superstition,' she says, 'but best come home straight away anyway.'

The dog leads the way. I love this dog. She takes me down her favourite trails, waiting, panting at forks in the trail. I see a deer. A small one with little white spots. An impossible sight in this day and age, but here she is in this magical forest.

We end up at a waterfall. The sun shafts through the

gorge, picking out trembling water drops. I take off my
shoes, sit on a boulder and watch ash seeds fall in golden
twists. There is a frayed blue rope on the far side where kids
jump into the pool in summer. Everything is green, mossy
and cold. The tree roots creep to the water's edge; quiet dark
holes lead under the earth.

And I am a part of all of this. I suddenly feel like I belong
here. It feels like the forest and the water know that I'm here
and who I am. I take off my clothes, take a big breath and
slip under the water.

It's icy cold, but worth it just for the afterglow when I
get out. On my way home I find Finn out with his
mushroom basket. We pick our way through the forest,
along mossy banks, over rotting logs, our eyes constantly
sweeping.

We sit for a while on a fallen tree, high up, our legs
dangling over the edge. Finn asks me, 'Now if you were to
change yourself into something else, how would you go
about doing that?'

I think of waterfall swimming and the secret feeling that
has given me inside, how if I did that every day something
would change. I say, 'Shapeshifting you mean? Or alchemy?
The turning yourself into gold thing?'

He nods, 'All of that.'

We are quiet, and it seems as if the whole forest bends in
to hear us.

Finn says, 'This forest has been designed by mushrooms.
They are linked into all the roots and everything is talking
right now, under this ground. If I can find the mushroom
that's connected to the root system, then maybe I can talk to

the trees as well. Kind of like being me and also shapeshifting into a tree.'

I tell him about the waterfall and say maybe I should be drinking that water too, then it would become part of me. Maybe if I drank enough of it, I could feel the things the waterfall can.

Maybe I could become part waterfall.

I realise there are a lot of experiments going on in this forest. I remember Ted's moss recorder hidden in here somewhere. Finn says, 'Ted thinks that if you talk to the trees enough one day they will talk back. He comes out here all the time for a chat, and he's trying to catch the moss out with his voice recorder.'

I wonder which of the boys will enter into the forest kingdom first, or indeed if they already have. I also wonder what entrance way I could take to enter this kingdom.

On the weekend Jenny drops me off at Glendalough while she visits her friend down the road. It is the biggest tourist stop in all of Ireland. Tour buses fill the lanes and the parking bays. There are knitting shops and tea shops clustered around the entrance.

But once inside there is an astonishing quiet stillness. The land seems to absorb the tourists into itself, and I don't notice them any more. I put my hand on St Kevin's round tower. The grey stone is warm and smooth. It is here where St Kevin kneeled, his arms outstretched in prayer, and a blackbird mistook him for a tree and laid its egg in his hand. St Kevin stayed there, kneeling, still and silent until the baby bird hatched and flew away. A saint for our times, I think.

I walk through the long grass past the tower and around the lower lake, sending butterflies spinning. And it feels like

St Kevin is still up there. Maybe he is always here in some form, holding the world steady for the blackbirds. Maybe St Kevin found his way into the magical kingdom the boys at home are after.

Jenny asks me about my Irish family, but really I have nothing to say. Dad made sure to cut the ties. We visited once when I was young. I have some hazy memories but that's it.

'Don't go back Sarah, don't go back,' he insisted. And now, here I am, circling back, trying to pick up what was lost.

Jenny lends me her car, she tells me to visit my grandparents' graves, to walk the lanes, sit beside the river, and listen to the land. She says I can have as much time off as I want.

I go straight to Ardee. And I remember. I am shocked that I remember. The way the road curves past Grandma's cottage, the church on the corner, the river. The feeling of being a little girl, in a back seat with an agitated father driving. The sight of soldiers on the street, their guns raised.

I park the car in the church car park. At the entrance there is a giant yew tree. A furious little girl is beating the tree with a stick. Her mum kneels down. 'Don't make the tree cry,' she says.

'But where are its eyes?' her girl yells. 'You have to have eyes to cry with and this tree has none.'

Her mum strokes the tree trunk, and she leans against it. 'You don't need eyes to cry,' she says.

I try to find the old house. It's not there; it was just a tumbling-down shack 30 years ago so I guess it hasn't stood the test. The town looks horrible. Grandad was on the town council here so I berate him in my head. 'Why didn't you divert the trucks, Grandad?' I yell. 'Why didn't you make this place better?'

Surprisingly, I hear back from him. 'There were other things!' he thunders. 'There were troubles worse than trucks.'

I walk down to the Dee. Half my dad was released into this river when he died. Mum came with the urn, but only managed to scatter half. The rest of him goes to New Zealand. I wave to half of him, but then realise he has long gone out to sea. He's not the type to swim back up, to return to the breeding ground like a wild salmon. Or a merman.

Newgrange is close, so I go. It is startling. It feels alive, and it feels like my ancestors are right here. Right here. There are spirals, suns, triangles carved into the stones, and I try to figure out what they say. Suddenly it seems important to know. This is not just ancient art any more. These are my people who have written on these stones.

In the visitor centre there are diagrams showing stones being rolled, then hoisted to stand upright. It all looks very, very unlikely. 'Some scientists' mad imaginations,' I mutter to the person next to me.

It seems more likely these stones were lifted by music, by a fairy's magic pipe. Or maybe Queen Maeve sang them up. I think of the magic horn that shattered the walls of Jericho, and wonder if you could put that in reverse, would it lift these stones? I wonder why magic can't be taken seriously in a museum.

I drive through the Boyne Valley, stopping at places I remember, stopping to try to feel the land. I drive to the coast, to Annagassan. It was here that my grandma used to come. I have an old photo and an old memory of her here, a little old lady with no teeth, gleefully collecting seaweed. She would look to the mountains of the north that her whole life was spent fighting for.

I remember her singing 'Amazing Grace' here, and I remember her crying. For her land and her family that was all ripped apart. For those mountains are ours and not ours. For the family that she knows yet knows nothing about.

Now I sit on the wharf and eat sugar donuts in this time of peace and plenty. There is good seaweed today. I wish I could take it to Grandma. But I have no family here now, and no land to take it back to. I realise this land is mine and not mine.

On the supermarket notice board is a sign advertising 'Sacred Circle Dance'. My hostel is so grim in the evenings that to get out to dance is a good thing so I go. The Sacred Circle is run by nuns who can't dance or follow directions but who can sway and hold their hearts and that is enough. We hold hands and circle the flowers and candles in the middle of the dance floor.

At half time the lights come on and we all have a cup of tea and a chocolate biscuit. Sister Claire tells me this dance is the most holy thing I can be doing. She looks like she loves a good gossip. She sits beside me and says, 'Now who is it, on your money in New Zealand?'

I tell her, 'The Queen.'

She draws her breath, clutches my arm and leans in. She whispers things about sovereignty, she says she feels sorry for me. She starts to rock.

I offer up my credentials. I say, 'My dad wouldn't get a

New Zealand passport because he wouldn't swear allegiance to the Queen.'

Sister Claire jumps up, she cheers, raises her arm in the air and announces this Good News.

The dance becomes much wilder in the second half. There is puffing. Hair becomes loose. The swaying is forceful, the candles flicker and I feel a rush of love for these old women who have held so strong.

I arrive back to the farm in time for a sizzling plate of mushrooms and the last of the summer tomatoes. 'We saved these for your homecoming,' Jenny says. Everyone scrapes their chairs up to the table for the grand feast.

Ted isn't there. 'Our brother has become nocturnal,' says Grace. 'He has a new theory, he thinks the moss talks at night, so he spends all his nights up there listening. He sleeps at home during the day.'

It's nice to be back, with all of this life and all of this good humour. I would be happy staying and working, but Grace and Finn have booked themselves on a permaculture course at Sligo, on the west coast. They offer me a ride over with them.

'Come with us and visit Queen Maeve,' says Grace. 'She's resting up in Knocknarea; she'd love a visit.'

I'm a bit nervous about asking Jenny for more time off but she has given up pretending I am there for work. And I think work means something different to her. It just means living well, living in layers like the forest, as she keeps telling me.

We drive across the country, stopping at Loughcrew so I can look at the burial mounds there. The mountains here were made by the Cailleach, the Divine Hag. She dropped stones from her apron as she strode around, making mountains. She is everywhere, this Hag.

We go into the tea shop and I sign for the key to the ancient burial mounds. It costs nothing, there are no guides, no restrictions, no other people. Grace and Finn stay in the tea shop eating cake, but I put the key around my neck and climb up the hill.

The mist is down, the wind is up and my ears are red and aching with the cold. I unlock the iron gate and crawl into the 5000-year-old passage chamber.

And it's just me.

I sit cross-legged encased in tons of heavy rock. It's warm and silent and dark and strangely comforting. After a while I lie down, face to the earth. I breathe it in and I listen. I try to remember what the land remembers.

Outside, the mist has turned to heavy rain. I half slide down the hill and into the tea shop. Grace has bad news: she has looked up the weather forecast and it's solid rain for the next two weeks. The whole of the permaculture course will have to be indoors. The two of them look gloomy. They tell me to take the car and go south, where the weather will be better, then meet them back in Sligo and we can drive home together.

So I drop them off at their course and drive down to Connemara National Park. Grace is right: the skies are clear down here and Diamond Hill shines out. The heather has dried off, the flowers have become golden seed heads and everywhere is orange.

A fine day is a busy day on this mountain. There is a trail of us silhouetted on the ridgeline; the tourists, the diaspora.

We sit on rocks at the top, quietly looking over the land and over the sea to America.

It looks idyllic from this high up; there are fishing villages and white cottages and green fields. But this was famine country. The fields look green but they grow little. We all know that we could be in famine country again, not just here but in our own lands too. All our soils are poor, all our oceans depleted.

The Green Festival is on in Letterfrack, and I join a wild foods walking tour that Sean leads. We suck honey out of fuchsia flowers, crouch down to see wild garlic and witch elm seeds, and we breathe in the earth.

'This wild food lifts the heart,' Sean says. 'The gathering and the eating of wild things lifts the heart like nothing else.'

He talks of beech leaves infused in gin, dandelion honey, elderflower wine, and honey mead. He takes us inside the visitor centre's classroom. He makes us lime flower tea and we eat chestnuts in chocolate. The walls are covered in botanical drawings and at the back there are some stuffed birds. A little owl, a cormorant. This is a classroom of the 1970s, untouched and immensely reassuring.

He stands at the front of the room and talks to us. 'This land used to be oak forest from coast to coast. We are really people of the woods. But now we love our bog and it doesn't even grow anything. That's what you people should do too. Love your land. Put your face to the earth and breathe it in. Sing it songs. Tell it stories. Listen to what it tells you. The land remembers and it wants to be loved.'

The coastline here is filled with little bays and I spend a lot of time walking them. 'Good seaweed here, Grandma,' I say to her and to the wind.

I walk down to Mannin Bay. It's a long walk down a track, the sea on one side, the bog on the other. I hear snorting, then a grey seal head rises out of the water. She looks straight at me. She looks just like a woman, a worldy-wise woman, sighing and breathing and tossing her head. She knows what love is, this seal, what it is to lie down in a human bed, to love a scraggle of children.

Behind her there are mountains, blue water, golden seaweed and a low sun. She looks into my eyes. And this moment is the most important thing the world has ever seen. The answer to all the questions is here. It is a seal breathing.

I lean over the bridge, and an old man joins me. We are silent, we watch her. Then he starts to sing. His song calls out to her; she breathes some more, her eyes fixed on us. I join in the chorus and we weave some magic together, the three of us.

When we stop, the seal slips under the water and all is quiet. I turn to him and ask, 'Do you think that was a selkie?'

He is quiet. He leans on the bridge and looks across the water to the mountains. 'They say not,' he sighs, 'but, still, it's important to sing.'

At Doolin I walk the cliffs of Moher. Here the cliffs drop straight down to the sea from an astonishing height. I have a good few hours walking on my own before I get to the visitors centre and all the tour buses. The centre is packed, but it's warm inside and I like looking around exhibits. 'The Changing Earth' and 'The Changing Climate' displays are both blank and have a sign saying 'Out of Order'.

I read tales of men climbing over the cliffs on ropes to get birds' eggs, of girlfriends sitting in the grass looking out to sea for their sweethearts to return. Leaving and returning stories are drenched in this place, with the sea just there, and America just a bit further on.

It feels like the whole Irish diaspora is here in this room with me. It is crowded and we all want a turn on the computer. 'Type in your family name and get your history' the sign says. We may not have a family here any more, but we all have a name. And that is enough for the computer.

Hearts and eyes yearn for the stories, the music, the things we don't know any more. It takes one generation to lose things, they say, and everyone in here feels that loss. We are all from lands that have other roots, ones we don't belong to. But here, in this room, we can find some ancestry, some belonging.

At night Doolin turns into a music mecca. I go to Fitzpatrick's pub where there is a traditional music session going on. Whoever wants to play can join in. Tonight there are eleven musicians. Some are from here, some are not. Tom, the man who runs the hostel, is here, playing his fiddle.

I say, 'It's really nice of you guys to let anyone play here.'

He replies, 'Sure these people are not just anyone; they are our forgotten ones, returning home for a while. We all want to bind ourselves together again. That's what our music does.'

He is right. When the music starts whirling, we all get pulled in. The lateness of the night doesn't matter, nor does the infertile fields, the wind, the hard life, the loss. It doesn't matter that we all come from different lands now, for we are bound together in this pub with this music and this firelight, and it is glorious and heartbreaking all at the same time.

Back at Sligo it's still raining, and Grace and Finn are in

the final days of their course. There are lots of things for me to do here, though, even in the rain. Besides, just sleeping with Queen Maeve on guard up there on the mountain is enough. They say she is buried standing up, her arm raised ready to go into battle.

I have heard stories of Maeve all my life, and Grace has added more. She is Queen of the Fairies, Goddess of the Land, a Queen who married many, many times. A Queen who is real and not real.

At the local shop there are free maps of the walking track to the top of Knocknarea. The pamphlet says Maeve likes you to take a rock up to her. Down at the shore I call out to the rocks, 'Who wants to come? Who wants to be with Queen Maeve?'

I sit and wait. The sun comes out and a small white pebble gleams. I pick it up, hold it in my pocket and sleep with it under my pillow. I am pleased it is little. I don't think I could carry anything bigger up there. The rocks at the top have been rolled up from miles away, the geologists say. But I have no strength to roll up rocks; I have no magic pipe to sing them up either.

The next morning it is fine. I walk straight up the mountain, through the forest and through the wind. Maeve's tomb is huge. I am shocked by its size, as from below it looks small, but up here it is a mountain on top of a mountain. This Queen must be a mighty force.

Her tomb is still sealed. I lay my pebble to rest on the edge of the cairn, I open my flask of honey mead, pour a little out on the earth for Maeve, and sit down for a talk.

Stories tell of Maeve being married many times, to king after king, for to marry her was to marry the land itself. I figure Maeve must have had some pretty wild proposals, much wilder than mine, so she is the perfect one to ask for advice.

I tell her of my proposals. The funny ones, the ones that I almost pursued, the crazy ones, the ones I could go back for.

I tell her that I've been thinking Mr Right may not make everything right. That there may be lots of Mr Rights. Or Ms Rights. Or none at all. I ask her what I should do.

I sit quietly while the mist swirls and shreds itself; sometimes I see bits of the sea way down there. I sip honey mead and I think about home.

Suddenly I realise that's what I need. My own home and my own land.

I need to go home.

I need to fall in love with my own land. Not with any Mr or Ms Right. I need to stop looking for proposals and look to what is right at my feet. I need to put down my travelling bags and commit to my own land. I need to marry it, to lie down on it and breathe it into me, to find a place for its wildness to live inside me. I need to kneel on it, to stretch out my arms and let the birds nest in my hands. I need to be like St Kevin.

I need to be like Queen Maeve.

The land is the important thing and mine is missing me. I know it is. I need to listen for the songs the rocks sing, to drink the waterfalls, to breathe in the smell of the earth.

I stand up and look out over this stretch of sea that my home lies at the end of. That's where my heart is and that's where I'm going. I hurry down the mountain. Halfway down, a stream gushes. I stop, crouch down and listen. I lean in and tell it my plans. For this is my business now.

I am in the business of rivers, mountains and dark crumbling earth. Of narrow tracks and fallen leaves. Of moss and mushrooms.

I am in the business of home.

## THE END

*May the road rise up to meet you.*
*May the wind be always at your back.*
*May the sun shine warm upon your face;*
*the rains fall soft upon your fields and until*
*we meet again,*
*may God hold you in the palm of His hand.*

— OLD IRISH BLESSING

# About the Author

Sarah Dunne lives in a regenerating forest in New Zealand. She is in the process of re-wilding herself and re-wilding the land.

Contact Sarah at sarah.dunne.author@gmail.com

facebook.com/sarah.dunne.author

Printed in Great Britain
by Amazon